VOLUME 20

Uakari

FUNK & WAGNALLS WILDLIFE ENCYCLOPEDIA

GENERAL EDITORS • Dr. Maurice Burton and Robert Burton

Also published as The International Wildlife Encyclopedia and
Encyclopedia of Animal Life.
Funk & Wagnalls, Inc., New York, New York

Tiger

Tiger

One of the largest of the 'big cats', the tiger's sinuous grace, splendid carriage and distinctive colouring make it one of the most magnificent of all animals. A large male averages 9 ft—9 ft 3 in. in length including a 3ft tail. It stands 3 ft or more at the shoulder and weighs 400—500 lb. Females are a foot or so less in length and weigh about 100 lb less. The various races of tigers vary considerably in size from the small Bali Island tiger to the outsized tiger found in Manchuria which may reach 12 ft in total length. The ground colour of the coat is fawn to rufous red, becoming progressively darker southwards through the animal's range, the Balinese tiger being the darkest. The underparts are white. There have been rare cases of white tigers in India. The coat is overlaid with black to blackish-brown transverse stripes, and these contrasting colours provide an excellent camouflage in forest regions.

In cold climates such as Siberia and Manchuria, tigers have thick, shaggy coats which become shorter and denser in the warmer climates. The hair round the face is longer than on the rest of the body, forming a distinct ruff in adult males.

From its original home in Siberia, the tiger spread across almost the whole of Eurasia during the Ice Ages. Today it is found only in Asia where a number of geographical races are recognised, including those of Siberia, Manchuria, Persia, India, China, Sumatra, Java and Bali. The races differ only in size, colour and markings.

◁ Overleaf: menacing snarl—wild Indian tiger.
◁ Transport solution: a helpless tiger cub is carried in the same way as a domestic kitten.
▷ Solitary splendour: tiger caught by flash.

Peter Jackson: Photo Res

Solitary prowler

Although its original home was in the snowy wastes of Siberia the tiger's natural preference is for thick cover It has, however, become adapted to life in rocky mountainous regions, the reed beds of the Caspian, and the dense steaming jungles of Malaya and islands such as Java and Bali. It cannot, however, tolerate excessive heat and during the heat of the day it will lie up in long grass, caves, ruined buildings, or even in swamps or shallow water.

The tiger is an excellent swimmer and in times of flood has been known to swim from one island to another in search of food. Unlike most members of the cat family it is not a good climber and seldom takes to the trees, but there is a record of a tiger taking a single leap of 18 ft from the ground to pull a man off a tree. Its hearing is very good and is the sense most used in stalking prey. It does not appear able to see unmoving animals, even at a short distance.

The tiger has a variety of calls ranging from a loud 'whoof' of surprise or resentment to a full-throated roar when disturbed or about to launch an attack.

Strength widens the menu

A tiger preys on deer, antelope, wild pig and smaller animals such as monkeys and porcupines. It will take fish and turtles in times of flood and locusts in a swarm. It occasionally attacks larger animals such as wild bull buffaloes, springing on their backs and breaking their necks. When food is short it may steal cattle, and an old or injured tiger too weak to hunt may attack humans. Game is, however, its natural food and it is interesting that tigers have completely deserted some forested areas of India where game animals have disappeared even though there were still plenty of wandering cattle about.

A tiger stalks using stealth for the first part of its hunt, finally attacking with a rush at its victim, grasping a shoulder with one paw and then seizing the throat. It then presses upwards, often breaking the neck in the process. After a kill it withdraws to a secluded spot, preferably under cover, taking its prey with it. If it cannot do this, or hide its kill near its lying-up place, it is forced to have a hurried meal and leave the rest of the carcase to the hyaenas and vultures and other carrion eaters.

Small striped cubs

Only while the tigress is in season do male and female tigers come together; according to some authorities, this could be for less than two weeks. During this time a tiger will not allow another male near him and will fight, sometimes to the death, over possession of the female. In India the mating season is variable, but in Malaya it is from November to March and in Manchuria it is during December. A female starts to breed at about 3 years of age and then has a litter every third year, or sometimes sooner. After a gestation of 105–113 days, 3–4 cubs are born, occasionally as many as 6. The mortality among cubs is high and usually no more than two survive to adulthood. They are born blind and helpless, weighing only 2–3 lb, but they have their parents' distinctive striped pattern from the beginning. The cubs grow rapidly; their eyes open after 14 days and they are weaned at 6 weeks. At 7 months they can kill for themselves, but stay with their mother until 2 years old, during which time she trains them in hunting. They are fully grown at 3 years.

Man the hunter

Although the tiger has few natural enemies it has been hunted by man from very early times, at first by the local people and later for sport. In India especially, the coming of the British and the introduction of firearms was disastrous to the tiger and it is estimated that in 1877 alone 1 579 tigers were shot in British India. Today the reduction of game animals and the reduction of its natural habitat is further diminishing its numbers, and as a result six of the eight races of tiger are listed as being in danger of extinction.

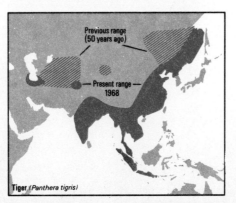

Tiger (Panthera tigris)

△ Reflected glory: unlike many of the cat family, tigers often take to the water and are strong swimmers. In times of flood they have been known to feed on fish and turtles and to swim in search of stranded prey. They cannot bear excessive heat and will sometimes sit in shallow water in an attempt to keep cool.

Man the hunted

Tigers have a respect and fear for man which is difficult to explain. Even if harassed by curious humans or sportsmen a tiger will not normally react until its patience is well-nigh exhausted. Normally a man can walk in a tiger's habitat without fear or hindrance and there have been several instances of a tiger approaching a man while sitting quietly near his camp and passing by, doing no harm even though it was obvious that it had seen him. Men have been followed for many miles by tigers and have come to no harm; they were probably being escorted off the territory. It is only when its normal hunting routine is disturbed that it becomes really dangerous. It may then become a man-eater, especially when shot at indiscriminately, incapacitating it rather than killing it. A wounded tiger left to its fate, without the strength to hunt, will resort to man-eating or cattle killing, out of necessity, as it will when injured by natural mishap. One of the commonest causes of injury is damage by porcupine quills. If the quills enter the paws or lower limbs the tiger cannot pull down and kill natural prey or cattle. Occasionally the quills may even penetrate the tiger's jaw and the animal starves to death. Old age may also cause a tiger to attack cattle or humans. Once a tiger has turned man-eater or cattle-killer, for whatever reason, every man's hand is against it. Whole villages will turn out and not rest until it is killed, even in areas where the tiger is protected by law.

class	**Mammalia**
order	**Carnivora**
family	**Felidae**
genus & species	***Panthera tigris***

Tiger moth

Not all tiger moths have markings like a tiger but all their caterpillars are hairy and so are called woolly bears. For this reason the whole family is known as the Arctiidae, from the Greek **arctos**, meaning a bear. This family also includes the footman or ermine moths which lack the very bold markings and coloration characteristic of the true 'tigers'. In continental Europe the moths themselves are called 'bears' rather than 'tigers', by reference to their larvae.

The most typical members of the group belong to the genus **Arctia**, one of which is the common and gaudy garden tiger moth **Arctia caja**. The garden tiger is 1 in. long with a wingspan of nearly 3 in., the males being slightly smaller. The forewings are cream coloured with bold dark brown to black markings and the hindwings are red with large black spots with deep blue centres. Not all garden tigers have markings recalling those of tigers but they are very variable and in some individuals the markings are tiger-like. This is even more true of other species of tiger moths. So variable are the markings that no two individuals of a species are quite alike, and on any individual the pattern of the left wings will be different from the pattern of the right wings.

Another common species is the cream-spot tiger **A. villica**. **A. quenseli** lives in the Arctic and also high up in the Alps and **A. hebe** is a southern European moth. The Jersey tiger **Euplagia quadripunctaria** and the brilliantly coloured scarlet tiger **Panaxia dominula**, another European species, are sometimes placed in a separate family, the Hypsidae.

A few true tigers, including **Arctia caja**, are found in North America, but the characteristic tiger moths of the region belong to the genus **Apantesis**, which is almost confined to that continent. These occur in great variety and on the forewings of almost all of them they display a distinctive pattern of pale streaks on a dark background.

▽ Cloaked in the long brown, black and white hairs that have given it its name, a garden tiger moth caterpillar nibbles a nettle leaf. These larvae are less fussy than most in their diet and will eat almost any succulent plant leaves —a few will eat leaves of woody plants.

Wandering ravenous larvae

The caterpillars of most tiger moths feed on low-growing plants of various kinds, and that of the garden tiger is content with almost any fairly succulent leaves that it encounters, such as weeds and cultivated plants. When they are ready to pupate, these very hairy larvae, and also those of the allied ermine moths, always wander for several hours before settling down to spin their cocoons. They may often be seen crossing roads and, for caterpillars, they travel remarkably fast. The moths themselves also run over the ground and do so fast enough to be sometimes mistaken at first glance for a mouse. Often a kitten will play with one, so drawing its owner's attention to the moth. The wandering habit of the caterpillars was noticed in England as much as 400 years ago and this is recorded in Topsell's *Book of Serpents*, published in 1608. At that time they were called 'beare-worms' and also 'palmer worms', by reference to the palmers or mendicant friars, 'which doo wander and stray hither and thither and consume and eat up that which is none of their owne' — a description which fits the caterpillars equally well. In the United States the name 'palmer worm' is given to *Ypsolophus pometellus*, a relative of one of the clothes moths which also wanders and sometimes causes considerable damage to fruit trees.

The pupa is enclosed in a cocoon of silk in which larval hairs, shed at the time of spinning the cocoon, are mixed.

The hairs of these larvae may cause some irritation, but do not have the poisonous and urticating properties of some of the other hairy caterpillars, notably those of the tussock moths, Lymantridae. They are, however, sufficient to deter almost all birds from eating them, the exception being the cuckoo, which swallows them without hesitation, ejecting the hairs from time to time in the form of pellets.

Idly resting on a leaf, a male garden tiger moth of the darker variety, displays the individual and distinctive brown and white markings on its wings.

PH Ward

Artificial tiger moths

The extremely variable wing markings of the garden tiger has led to unusual effects. The forewings are occasionally entirely white or entirely dark brown, and the blue-black spots on the red hindwings may be almost absent or may spread, so the red is masked altogether. The moth is easy to rear as the larvae can be fed both in summer and winter on cabbage, and will breed continuously, generation after generation, if kept warm. Some of the more unusual individuals have appeared only in captive broods and so are really artificial productions, like fancy pigeons or breeds of cattle. Since their characters are usually inherited according to the precise laws of heredity, these varieties are of value in the study of genetics.

Stinging moths

The gaudy colours of the tiger moths play a definite part in protecting the insects from birds, as they advertise the fact that the moth is distasteful or even poisonous. If a resting garden tiger moth is molested or irritated it raises its forewings, displaying the bright red hindwings, and at the same time exposes a fringe of red hairs behind the head. These are not empty threats for a sub-stance resembling the poison acrylycholine is secreted in glands in the thorax and another dangerous poison can be extracted from its body fluids. If a tiger moth is roughly handled the sharp spines or spurs on the legs may become contaminated with the poison and act as a sort of sting, but only people with very delicate skin are affected.

phylum	**Arthropoda**
class	**Insecta**
order	**Lepidoptera**
family	**Arctiidae**

A warning from a female garden tiger moth as she exposes the fringe of red hairs behind her head and displays her boldy marked hindwings.

Tilapia

Tilapia is the name given to a hundred or so species of freshwater fishes which belong to the large family of cichlids. One species **Tilapia galilaea** *was probably responsible for the miraculous draught of fishes mentioned in the Bible. Other species are also used as food fishes and have been spread around the world. Tilapias are also kept as aquarium fishes and their study has brought to light several unusual features of fish behaviour.*

They have large heads and deep bodies, strongly compressed from side to side. The long dorsal fin is spiny in front and soft-rayed in the hinder part, which usually rises to a point in the rear. The anal fin is larger and pointed behind. The tail fin is squarish along its rear edge. The pectoral fins are moderately large and the pelvic fins are more or less level with them. Most tilapias grow to a length of 8–12 in. and a few species may be 18–20 in. long. The colour varies from species to species and is often very variable within a species. The back may be yellowish to olive-brown, green, bronze, blue or violet, the flanks silvery and the belly even lighter. Usually there is a metallic sheen of bronze, golden or violet, and the body and fins are often marked with darker spots and bars.

Tilapias are widely distributed over Africa south of the Sahara, and from the Nile basin to Israel, Jordan and Syria.

Peripatetic tilapias

Tilapias live in lakes and the sluggish parts of rivers, estuaries and brackish lagoons, especially where there is shelter under banks, among water plants or among water-logged branches. Large numbers of *Tilapia grahami* live in the soda lake Magadi, in Kenya, in water of 28–45°C/80–112°F. Tilapias readily acclimatise and several species have been transported all over central and eastern Africa; so many have become established in local rivers to which they are not native. There are five species now in Lake Victoria, for example, two native and three introduced. The precise mechanics of these introductions are not always known, so it is usual to speak of the fishes as having 'escaped'. For example, *T. mossambica*, of East Africa, turned up in Java in 1939. By various means, some of which can only be guessed at, it is now found in Sumatra, Bali, Lombok, Celebes, the Philippines, Taiwan and South Korea, as well as Malaya, Thailand and Ceylon. In the west it is established on Trinidad, St Lucia and Haiti and, recently, in Texas.

How they get there

In 1961 a press report told of tilapia 'turning up' in large areas of Florida. Apparently a biologist had suggested that they should be introduced into a pond to provide new sport for anglers, but that does not explain their being found in 16 lakes, 4 creeks and 2 rivers in southern Florida. The press

H Hansen

R Apfelbach

Gerald Cubitt

R Apfelbach

△ *Playing safe: young* **T. nilotica** *stay close to their mother; when danger threatens they all rush back into her mouth.*
△◁ *Mouth brooder: a female* **Paratilapia multicolor** *with young fry showing through the cheeks of her brood pouch — the young are released as soon as they can swim.*
◁ *Aggression not affection: male* **T. variabilis** *fight each other by pushing with their mouths.*
▽◁ *Small shoal of blue-grey tilapia in the clear water of the Mzima springs in Kenya.*

report gives a clue when it continues, that although it is illegal to put tilapia into waters that are free of them, many tropical fish fanciers tire of having them in their aquaria and dump them in the nearest water. Since tilapia has 'an elephant's appetite and a rabbit's reproductive ability' it is not long before it cleans out a pond of food needed by other fish. This is a danger that has to be watched, and in some places native fishes have been wiped out after tilapias have been introduced. On the other hand, several of the larger species, including *T. mossambica*, are an important source of protein, and are often bred in special ponds.

Artificial ponds

In 1951 *T. melanopleura* was established in special fish ponds in Madagascar. These were so successful that more ponds were made. By 1958 there were 40 000, by 1960, 80 000. An adult could catch 11 lb of these fish a day, and even a child could catch 4 lb a day. In South Africa, where tilapias are called kurper or freshwater bream, they are used to clear sewage ponds of mosquito larvae, and at the same time they multiply and the young can be transferred to other ponds and rivers to provide food fishes. One problem that occurs when the tilapia multiply rapidly is that they eat up the vegetation and insect larvae, starve out or eat up the other fishes, and in the end the pond is

overstocked with undersized tilapias. A suggested cure is to use hatcheries and to separate the sexes, putting the females in one pond and the males in another. In one experiment *T. mossambica* were crossed with other species of *Tilapia* and the hybrids were all males — which could be grown to maturity for food without the problems of a population explosion.

Mainly plant eaters

Tilapias are basically vegetarian, some species sieving the plant plankton, others eating the small algae on stones, and a few doing both. Some seem to turn readily to animal food, such as water insects and their larvae, or fish fry — even tilapia fry.

Mouth nurseries

Some tilapias lay their sticky eggs on the surface of a stone which the male and female have carefully cleaned beforehand. Once the eggs are laid the male swims over them and sheds his milt to fertilise them. The parents aerate the eggs by fanning them with their fins, and when the fry have hatched the female keeps them together in a tiny shoal, shepherding them by signals until they are old enough to swim away on their own. Most tilapias are, however, mouth brooders. To start with the pair dig a pit an inch or two deep and 5 – 12 in. across in the sandy bottom, scooping up mouthfuls of sand or small pebbles and spitting them a little way from the nest. Then the male swims head downwards and mouths the bottom of the pit. Soon he starts to swim slowly over the nest, rubbing it with his belly. The female joins in and they take turns in swimming across it. Finally the female lays her eggs and the male sheds his milt over them. This is repeated several times and when all the eggs are laid either the male or the female, or both — the pattern varies with the species — suck the eggs into

the mouth. The eggs hatch in the mouth and 8 – 20 days later the fry leave it and swim away. In some species the female first sucks up the eggs and then the milt as the male sheds it, so that the eggs are fertilised in her mouth.

Careful tests made with one species showed that if the eggs are removed from the mouth of a mouth brooder they fail to hatch and become diseased. It was finally discovered why: the movement of the eggs in the throat makes them rub against each other and against the sides of the pouch, and this cleans them of any bacteria that might damage them.

Counts have shown that tilapia begin to spawn at 2 – 3 months, may spawn 6 – 11 times a year, and that some species multiply 1 000 times in 2 – 3 months.

Miraculous draught

Tilapias are today an important item of food in tropical countries. Paintings on Egyptian antiquities show they were fished thousands of years ago. The miraculous draught of fishes recorded in the Bible was almost certainly tilapias. Canon Tristam, writing over a century ago, told of seeing *Tilapia galilaea* 'in shoals of over an acre in extent, so closely packed that it seemed impossible for them to move, and with their dorsal fins above the water. They are taken both in boats and from the shore by nets run deftly round, and enclosing what one may call a solid mass at one swoop, and very often the nets break'. A man was stationed at a high point on shore to spot the shoals.

class	**Pisces**
order	**Perciformes**
family	**Cichlidae**
genus	*Tilapia*

Tinamou

The tinamous are partridge-like birds that present a fine puzzle; in spite of looking like small game birds they are probably more nearly related to large South American running birds, the rheas (p 1944). They range in size from a quail, 7 in. long, to a grouse, 14 in. long. They have rounded, bulky bodies in which the well-developed feathers on the rump often hide the very short tail feathers. The wings are short and rounded, the legs short, with the hind toe, or hallux, minute or missing. The head is small and the neck slender. The plumage is dull, brown or grey with spots and bands, so tinamous are extremely inconspicuous. They have some powder-down plumage, like herons and parrots.

The martineta or crested tinamou is large, about 14½ in. long. It is a dull mottled brown with a long crest that is spread when the bird is excited. The ornate tinamou also has a crest which can

be erected when excited. One of the smallest tinamous is the 9in. little tinamou. Its upperparts are rich brown with the sides of the head grey and the chin and throat white, gradually turning grey on the underparts of the tinamou.

The 50 or so species of tinamous live in the New World from southern Mexico to southern Chile and Argentina, including the island of Trinidad.

Accident prone birds

Tinamous live in a variety of habitats from wet rain forests to open scrubland and the ornate tinamou can be found at over 13 000 ft in the Andes. They spend most of their time on the ground, keeping in touch with each other by attractive, fluting calls. They take flight only when startled, suddenly exploding into the air with a rush of wings,

but they never fly far. Although their flight muscles are well-developed, sustained flight seems to be impossible because the heart and lungs are small. The tinamous' powers of co-ordination also seem to be limited as, when flushed, they sometimes hurtle head-long into branches and may kill themselves. Similarly, although fast runners, they soon tire and if pressed they may stumble. As tinamous are widely hunted for their extremely palatable flesh, it is surprising that these clumsy birds have survived; but they escape detection by remaining motionless or slipping quietly away through the under-growth, camouflaged by their drab plumage.

A wide diet

Tinamous feed mainly on plants, particularly seeds and fruit, but they also eat insects and other small invertebrates. The ornate tinamou eats more animal food than most tinamous, including beetles, caterpillars and grasshoppers. Occasionally tinamous have been seen eating larger animals, such as mice. The plant food includes small leaves, flowers, fruits, seeds and, very occasionally, roots.

△ *Grey outlook of a martineta tinamou.*

Father plays mother

Outside the breeding season tinamous are solitary. During the breeding season they are seen in twos and threes, and towards the end small coveys, consisting of parents with half-grown young, are formed. The breeding habits of tinamous are unusual in that the birds are usually polygamous and the females, which are slightly larger, with brighter colours than the males, play the dominant role in courtship. Some species live in pairs, as in the ornate tinamou where the sex ratio is 1:1, but in the variegated tinamou there are four times as many males as females. Each female may lay eggs in more than one nest, and several females may lay in a single nest. This is possible because the males build the nest and also incubate the eggs.

In the ornate tinamou courtship is fairly simple. The female is the most aggressive in defending the 6-acre territory and she courts the male by following him, both feeding as they go. The male displays by raising his rump and spreading the feathers to show a conspicuous dark patch. The variegated tinamou has a more elaborate courtship. The female runs to and fro, calling to attract the male and on approaching him, she lowers her wings and raises the tail and rump feathers to display a beautiful and elaborate pattern.

The male tinamou builds a nest in the undergrowth, which is little more than a poorly lined depression in the ground. The number of eggs that he incubates varies from 1 to 12 and they hatch in a little less than 3 weeks, a short period for the size of the bird. The male may sit so tight during incubation that he can be lifted off the nest. After the chicks have left the nest he stays with them and defends them.

Doubtful honours

Tinamous are probably preyed upon, as partridge and grouse are, by both birds of prey and ground predators, such as foxes and the small and medium-sized members of the cat family. Sportsmen rate them as one of the finest gamebirds—always an unhappy situation for a bird. Frozen tinamou have also been exported to the United States as 'South American quail'.

Rheas' little cousins

The tinamous are classed in their own order the Tinamiformes, low down in the scale of bird classification. They are not closely related to any other birds. Their resemblance to guineafowl, partridges and their relatives is only external, a consequence of their similar, ground-living habits. From a study of their anatomy it seems that tinamous are most closely related to the rheas, although the latter are flightless ratites, a group which includes ostriches and emus, that lack a keel on the breastbone. Yet the tinamous are 'carinates'. That is, they have a well-developed carina or keel on the breastbone, like the great majority of living birds. The breeding habits of tinamous are like those of rheas, with aggressive females and motherly males. There are physical similarities in the structure of the palate and in the shape of the rhamphotheca—the horny covering of the bill, and also there are chemical similarities in the composition of the eggs.

The relationship of tinamous and rheas suggests that tinamous are very primitive, originating from some very early ancestor of the modern birds.

class	**Aves**
order	**Tinamiformes**
family	**Tinamidae**
genera & species	***Crypturellus soui*** *little tinamou* ***C. variegatus*** *variegated tinamou* ***Eudromia elegans*** *martineta tinamou* ***Nothoprocta ornata*** *ornate tinamou, others*

John Tashjian at San Diego Zoo

Tit

Some of the 60-odd species of tits, known
in North America as titmice and chicka-
dees, are very familiar birds of garden and
woodland. They are usually classed in three
subfamilies, which may not be very closely
related. The largest group are the true tits
which are found in Europe, Asia, Africa
and North America. Another group are the
longtailed tits and bushtits and the third
are the penduline tits. The name is also
given to unrelated birds such as the bearded
tit or reedling (see parrotbill p 1706), the
shrike-tits, wren-tits, tit-babblers, titlarks,
tit-shrikes and several others.

The two best known of the typical tits are
the great tit and blue tit. The great tit,
found over much of Europe and Asia and
spreading into North Africa must be one
of the most intensively studied of all wild
birds, the black-headed gull (p 225)
perhaps being its closest rival. It is 5½ in.
long, greenish-blue above, yellow below
with black on the head and underside and
white on the cheeks. The blue tit is 4½ in.
long and is restricted to Europe and
neighbouring parts of Asia and North
Africa. It has a bright blue crown, wings
and tail, yellow underparts and white
cheeks. The best known of the American
tits is the blackcapped chickadee, 4½ in.
long and pale grey with a black head and
throat and white cheeks. Its plumage is not
very different from that of other chicka-
dees. In North America the name titmouse
is given to tits with small pointed crests.

The longtailed tits are found in Europe
and Asia and the closely related bushtits
are found in North America. Their habits
are similar to those of the true tits, as are
those of the penduline tits. One penduline
tit lives in Europe and Asia, one in North
America and six in Africa.

Bird tables save migrations

The tits that come into the garden attract our attention by their bright colours and the acrobatic skill with which they forage among the twigs and leaves for their food. This is best seen when tits come to bird tables where they hop about, readily hanging upside down to feed from strings of peanuts or halved coconut shells. Some tits may travel several miles each day from woods to feed at bird tables. When natural foods fail, the bird tables may become the mainstay of many tits and without them they may be forced to migrate. There are no regular migrations but tits have been known to travel long distances in winter — for example from Russia to Portugal — to escape cold weather and food shortage. Tits sometimes form mixed flocks in winter and longtailed tits are particularly easy to recognize with their distinctive long tails. Longtailed tits roost together, forming fluffy balls of feathers with just their long tails sticking out. They are more gregarious than other tits, and move about in family parties.

Hammering for food

In their woodland homes tits feed on a variety of small insects, spiders and seeds. The small animals are picked from leaves and twigs or removed from their hiding places by stripping bark or hammering open nuts and seeds. The quiet but persistent hammering that can often be heard in woods is the sound of a blue tit opening a pine cone or a great tit chiselling an acorn, held in one foot, to extract the animals hiding within or to get at the contents. In northern regions surplus food in autumn may be stored in crevices for use in winter.

In Europe, at least, caterpillars form the bulk of the food brought to nestling tits while seeds are the main food of tits in winter. Great tits also kill the young of other small birds on rare occasions and blue tits sometimes attack fruit and buds.

Nests as purses

All true tits nest in holes. A few, such as the willow tit, which is thought by some to be the same species as the blackcapped chicka-dee, are able to excavate their own holes in rotten timber. The abandoned nests of large birds, squirrels' dreys, old cans, holes in the ground and other cavities are sometimes used. In well kept gardens and woods such sites are at a premium and this is one reason why tits are so willing to use nest-boxes. A cup-shaped nest of moss and lined with hair and feathers is built by both sexes within the cavity. Tropical tits lay 3–4 eggs while those living in temperate latitudes lay from 15 to 16. The female alone incubates the clutch and she is fed by the male, who alights near the nest and calls to the female to come and be fed. The eggs hatch in about 2 weeks and the chicks stay in the nest for 18–21 days, being fed by both parents.

The longtailed tit builds an elaborate globular nest with a side entrance. The exterior is covered with lichen and the interior is lined with as many as 2 000 feathers. The penduline tit lives near water, feeding on the seeds of reeds in winter, and it makes a globular nest that hangs from twigs. Some

Eric Hosking

2368

of its African relatives build nests of tough plant material which are sometimes cut down and used as purses.

Tits' native wit

Birds, with the exception of parrots (p 1704), crows (p 583), and a few others, are not particularly intelligent, yet the tits show some remarkably intelligent behaviour. They are extremely adept at pulling up lengths of string to which food is attached. Several European species are known to do this. The bird pulls the string up with its bill then clamps it with its foot while it pulls another length up with the bill, and so on until the peanut, or whatever it is, is reached. One blue tit learned to pull up a 2ft length of string. This behaviour is undoubtedly learned rather than instinctive. In their natural feeding habits tits regularly co-ordinate the movements of the bill and feet when they hammer seeds, but they learn to use this natural dexterity for string-pulling remarkably quickly.

Another habit that tits easily learn is that of opening milk bottles and stealing the milk. This began in Britain in 1921 and spread across the country. The tits were, again, using a basic feeding behaviour, opening the milk bottles with the actions used for hammering nuts and tearing bark. The tits, however, learned to improve these actions and also where to find milk bottles — even learning to follow the milk carts.

class	**Aves**
order	**Passeriformes**
family	**Paridae**
genera & species	**Aegithalos caudatus** longtailed tit **Parus atricapillus** blackcapped chickadee **P. caeruleus** blue tit **P. major** great tit **P. montanus** willow tit **Remiz pendulinus** penduline tit others

△ *A favourite garden bird, the agile, rather bold blue tit originally lived in woodland.*

◁ *Overleaf: Opening tactics of a great tit. Both great tits and blue tits are exceptionally intelligent birds and have learnt to apply their natural feeding techniques to such things as opening milk bottles and matchboxes.*

◁ *A coal tit leaves the tin can sanctuary where it has built its nest, to collect more food for the female who incubates the eggs.*

▷ *Man-made feast: a small flock of great tits attack a wedge of fat and suet.*

▽ *A precarious meal. A great tit displays its acrobatic skills as it feeds on a string of nuts.*

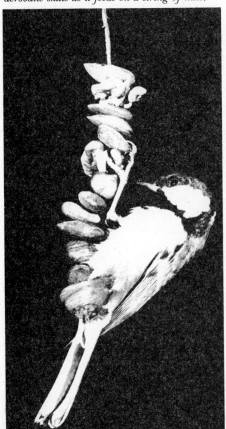

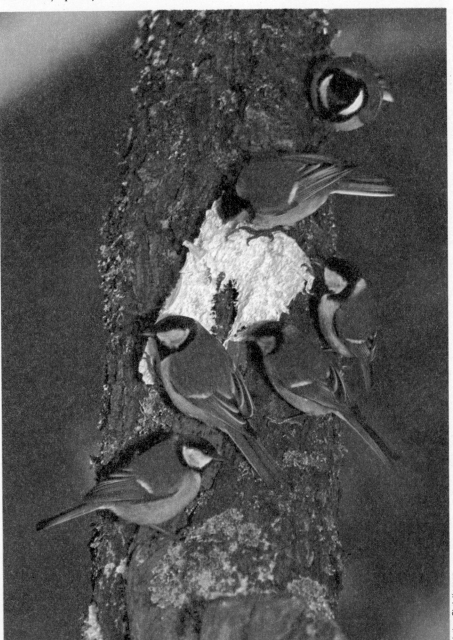

Titi

To most people who know it well the titi hardly looks like a monkey at all, with its short legs and bushy tail. It is, in fact, one of the most primitive of the South American monkeys, and it shares with the rest of them the wide-spaced, sideways-looking nostrils and the short and very monkeyish face. It is not very large, normally being 12—16 in. long in head and body with a tail of 13—20 in. It weighs about 1½ lb. A titi has long shiny fur which varies between grey and reddish brown from race to race.

As many as seven species and 33 sub-species have been named but today only two species are recognized. The dusky titi, the more widespread, ranges over most of the forest south of the Amazon. It is grey to dark brown, often with orange or reddish underparts. Its hands and feet are black or they may be the same colour as the rest of the limbs, and the tail is reddish or greyish. There may be a white tail-tip and possibly a grey or black band on the forehead. The second species, the widow monkey, is found around the tributaries of the upper Amazon, and is reddish-black with a white to orange patch on the throat, a black tail, black forearms and hindlimbs but usually whitish hands.

Daily hymn of hate

Titis usually live low in the trees, in pairs, each with one or two youngsters. Each pair holds a territory, in which there are favourite trees for feeding and sleeping. Almost every day there are conflicts at the borders of the territories. The occupants sit facing one another, calling at each other and take up a variety of aggressive postures, their hair standing on end, their backs arched and their tails lashing. The calls are mournful, wailing sounds. These conflicts, which help to maintain the territorial boundaries, are usually no more than a show of force, but they sometimes erupt into actual violence, one male chasing the other into his territory. While he is chasing the other male he may suddenly stop and mate with the opposing female! As well as defining its territory by a show of force the titi marks the boundary by rubbing the secretions of his chest gland along the branches. This scent-making usually takes place after the daily ritual of hurling insults and making faces at each other.

Carnivorous vegetarian

Titis have certain favourite feeding trees within their territories. They make their way to these after leaving the 'sleeping' trees, and again after the morning wailing match. Their food consists of fruit and some buds, as well as insects, birds' eggs, and even it is said some small birds which they creep up on unawares.

No guarantee of paternity

Many aspects of the titi's breeding cycle resemble those of marmosets (p 1421). The fact that titis live in mated pairs which

△ *The short, monkey-like face of a titi.*

▽ *Keeping in touch. A resting pair of dusky titis sit touching each other, their backs arched, hands and feet grasping the branch and their tails half-twined together helping them to balance.*

Chicago Zoological Society

San Diego Zoo

seem to be long-lasting—perhaps even permanent—restricts each male to one female, and ensures that a male looks after his own offspring—unless by chance his female has been fertilised by a more dominant male during a territorial chase. Just like marmosets, male titis carry the young, handing them to the female only for suckling. There seems to be no specific breeding season, although in eastern Colombia, William Mason, who studied the behaviour of titis in the wild, found a birth peak from December to March. Unlike marmosets, titis bear only one young at a time. It clings to its father with its hands, feet, and its tail, which is not, however, prehensile.

Mixed-up monkey

The titi is a New World monkey of isolated and primitive status. It has some anatomical similarities to marmosets, especially in its skull, teeth and skeleton. This may, however, be no more than two animals sharing certain primitive features. Its locomotion is also primitive, for although its legs are short, the hindlegs are relatively long and used for jumping. A titi does not, however, cling to vertical branches like other primitive primates such as bushbabies, tarsiers and some marmosets. Instead it sits on horizontal perches with the body hunched and all four feet together clutching the branch beneath, its tail hanging down behind. The male and female or an adult and young often sit side by side, huddled close with their tails intertwined. The titi is a nervous animal, with rapid, jerky movements and is of a restless temperament, continually jumping and running around. It does, however, have long periods of rest when the pair sit in contact, with their tails twined. They also occasionally groom one another but not as much as some primates.

Although classified in the same family, the titi is a very different type of monkey from a species such as the spider monkey (p 2228), with its prehensile tail and long arms, or the saki (p 2010) with its mobile fingers and long, comb-like incisors. It has been compared most closely to the douroucouli (p 663), but the characteristics it shares with this monkey are, like those it shares with marmosets, due to primitive characters surviving in both of them. So we are left with a 'mixture-monkey' that howls like a howler monkey, jumps like a squirrel monkey, and is in its social structure most like the smallest of the apes, the gibbon!

class	**Mammalia**
order	**Primates**
family	**Cebidae**
genus & species	*Callicebus moloch* dusky titi *C. torquatus* widow monkey

Toadfish

One species of toadfish makes a noise like a foghorn, and its relatives are celebrated for their noises. The toadfish's looks, too, are extraordinary; it has a head like a toad and the tail of a fish. Toadfishes have large heads, broad and somewhat flattened, with wide mouths armed with many blunt teeth. Tags of skin decorate the lower lip as well as other parts of the face. The eyes are large. The short, front dorsal fin is spiny and in some species the spines are hollow and poisonous. The second dorsal fin is long and soft-rayed. The pelvic fins lie well forward of the pectorals. Toadfishes are usually 1 ft long but may be up to 1½ ft. The scales are very small and are embedded in the slimy skin, usually a dirty brown colour with darker mottlings.

*There are about 30 species living mainly in shallow water in tropical and temperate seas, but some may enter brackish water, and a few live in freshwater. Included in the same family are the midshipmen of the genus **Porichthys** which have several hundred small light-organs on the underside of the body. These glow like the polished buttons on a midshipman's coat.*

Stay-at-home fishes

Toadfishes are solitary, slow-moving bottom-dwellers, usually sheltering among stones or rocks or in cavities. They are strongly territorial, each keeping to a fairly small area from which it drives away intruders of its own species. Toadfishes are also pugnacious towards almost any moving object. When experimentally teased with a stick they will snap at it or seize it between their teeth and hang on. Some toadfishes make limited migrations from deeper to shallower waters to breed, but as a family they are lethargic, so they require less oxygen than most fishes. They have only three pairs of gills and a small area of gill surface relative to the weight of the body. One result of their slow-moving ways is that they can live in water poorly supplied with oxygen; they can, if necessary, draw upon the oxygen in their swimbladder as a temporary measure.

Unofficial foghorn

One species especially, the oyster toadfish, which lives in shallow waters along the eastern coast of the United States, is famous for the sounds it makes. Other members of the family make sounds but the oyster fish has been singled out for study into the mechanisms. It has a heart-shaped swimbladder divided internally by a horizontal membrane and surrounded by a band of muscle. The inflated bladder is twanged by movements of the surrounding muscle, the membrane dividing its cavity probably acting like the velum of a drum. Sounds like grunts and growls as well as the louder foghorn noises are produced. Dr WN Tavolga has shown that at a distance of 2 ft the louder noises are comparable 'to the noise of a riveting machine or a subway train'. Water damps sound, so although a toadfish can be heard by anyone at the surface the sound reaching his ear is more like that from a distant fog horn. The grunts and growls seem to be used in territorial aggression and they often precede an attack, in which the toadfish uses its teeth. The foghorn sounds are less easy to explain but they are probably used to advertise, like bird song, the possession of a territory. They may also be used in breeding, perhaps to bring the male and female together.

Experiments have shown that if the muscle surrounding the swimbladder or the nerve supplying it are stimulated electrically, a swimbladder will emit grunts and growls after it is removed from the toadfish.

Fishy dustbins

Lethargic, bottom living fishes with wide mouths, toadfishes, as one would expect, snap up anything edible, including worms, shrimps, crabs, sea snails, small bivalves, squid and any fish that can be taken in at

△ *Apathy and lethargy reign among a group of toadfishes. These bottom-dwelling fishes usually take shelter wherever possible and are aggressive to almost anything that moves.*

one gulp. They also eat any carrion or offal, benefiting from man's waste as they do from his litter, for in coastal water toadfishes use tin cans and other such receptacles dumped in the sea as shelters from which to make their feeding sorties.

Zealous fathers

During June and July, the male oyster toadfish establishes a nest among rocks or stones, or in an old can, boot or other object lying on the seabed. Several females lay their eggs in it, to a total of 7–800. The eggs are $\frac{3}{16}$ in. diameter, amber-coloured, and sticky, and are laid in a single layer, carpeting the floor or the ceiling of the nest. During the 10–26 days before they hatch, the length of time needed depending on the temperature of the water, the male guards the nest, and he is unusually belligerent during this period. He also aerates the eggs by fanning them with his pectoral fins, and he keeps the nest clean. After hatching, the baby toadfishes stay in the nest for a while, until they are about 1 in. long. Then they leave the nest and cling to rock surfaces or to pebbles, by a sucker on their underside, but this disappears as they grow. They reach a length of $3\frac{1}{2}$ in. after one year.

The mystery tickings

Fishermen in various parts of the world have known for a long time that some fishes make sounds. There were those, for example, that were called drumfishes because of the noises they made, and there were those they nicknamed sea robins. The midshipman of the North American Pacific coast was called the singing fish. These were, however, regarded as exceptions, certainly by scientists, until the opening years of this century. What really gave a boost to the study of sounds made by fishes and other marine animals were experiences in World

War II, when submarine warfare became intensified and various types of mines came to be used, and when the development of frogmen attack meant that at any moment a warship might encounter some new form of attack or booby trap. Then, a toadfish lying at the bottom, making an unusual sound, might mislead, even spread something akin to panic, among a fleet of warships. Today, even more than then, the chances of an enemy using a new device has focussed attention on underwater sounds, so opening up a new field of knowledge.

class	**Pisces**
order	**Batrachoidiformes**
family	**Batrachoididae**
genera & species	**_Opsanus beta_** _Gulf of Mexico toadfish_ **_O. tau_** _oyster toadfish_ **_Porichthys notatus_** _Northern midshipman_ **_P. porosissimus_** _Atlantic midshipman others_

▽ *Open-mouthed, an oyster toadfish swims around, ready to snap up anything edible that it can take in at one gulp. They are sluggish fish and, although some make small migrations from deeper to shallower water, most are very lethargic and, as such, require less oxygen than most fishes. The toadfish therefore has only three pairs of gills which are smaller than usual. Toadfishes are able to survive in water poorly supplied with oxygen and can even live out of water for several hours, having a small reserve of oxygen in their swimbladders which they can draw upon in an emergency.*

Tody

Todies are small birds found only on a few islands of the West Indies. They are relatives of the motmots and are distantly related to the kingfishers, having rounded bodies and long bills. Todies are 3½—4 in. long and brilliantly coloured, the upperparts, wings and tail are a vivid green, and the underparts are whitish with a red patch on the throat, hence the Jamaican name of robin. They are yellow on the belly and usually pink on the flanks. The lower mandible is red and the three forward-facing toes are partly united by skin, as in kingfishers.

The five species are distinguished by the amount of pink on the breast and flanks, but the ranges of the species overlap in only one place, so they can be mainly identified by the place where they live. The overlap is on the island of Hispaniola, where in the eastern part of the Dominican Republic the ranges of the broad-billed and the narrow-billed todies coincide. The narrow-billed tody lives mainly in the humid mountain forests but is occasionally found in the more low-lying country which is the habitat of the broad-billed tody. It is, however, easily distinguished by its narrow bill, the bills of other todies being broad with fine serrations on the cutting edge of the upper mandible. The other todies are found on Cuba, Jamaica and Puerto Rico respectively.

Buzzing wings
Despite their brilliant colours, todies are easily overlooked because they are small enough to be hidden by single leaves, but they can easily be located by their harsh chattering or the buzz of their wings and flash of colour as they fly after insects. Todies are found mostly in damp woodland and forest, particularly in mountainous regions, but the broad-billed tody and, to some extent, the Puerto Rican tody are found in dry areas. Todies live in pairs, each holding a territory. When in flight they sometimes make a whirring noise with a special primary flight feather. Presumably this sound has something to do with courtship or territorial defence, as it is made by both sexes and is most often heard during the breeding season.

Fly-catching
The feeding habits of todies are very much like those of flycatchers. They perch on twigs, fairly near the ground, with their bodies upright and bills cocked, waiting for insects to fly by. As soon as one is spotted the tody flits out and catches it with an audible snap of the bill. The serrated edges of the upper mandibles, which are also possessed by motmots, are probably for crushing the hard bodies of insects. The narrow-billed tody also hops about among the leaves in search of food. The food of todies is almost exclusively insects, but they sometimes catch tiny lizards and probably other small ground vertebrates.

Hole-nesters
Although todies are numerous in many parts of the West Indies their nesting habits are not well known, at least partly because they nest in holes, as do motmots and kingfishers. The holes are excavated in low banks, perhaps only 1 or 2 ft high, and may be from a few inches to 2 ft long. Their diameter is about 1½ in. except for the terminal nest chamber which widens to about 3 by 5 in. Excavation is carried out by both

▽ *Despite its bright plumage, the tiny Jamaican tody is inconspicuous in the forest.*

JAL Cooke

sexes, one tody watching from a nearby perch while the other digs and loosens the soil with its long bill.

The two or three, sometimes four, white eggs, comparatively large for the size of the bird, are laid on the bare floor of the nest chamber. Nothing seems to be known about the care of the brood, but in their first plumage the fledglings lack the red patch on the throat.

Worn out with digging
There seems to be a good reason for the birds choosing low banks for their nesting holes. In Jamaica these are often at the sides of watercourses where in the rainy season there are rushing torrents. The banks vary from low weed covered mounds to clay cliffs 10—20 ft high, and it is noticeable that todies tunnel only into the low banks, where the soil is still moist from the rushing waters. That the cliffs are avoided because they are too hard seems likely from the observation made by a Mr Taylor, quoted by Lyddeker, who once saw a tody with 'almost the entire half or side of the upper mandible worn away; this was during a period of drought, when all vegetation was burnt and shrivelled, and the earth hard and unyielding.'

Once the birds have brought up their family, the nesting holes of todies are often taken over by other animals, especially mice, lizards and spiders.

Tame but not homely

Most accounts of todies describe how trusting and inquisitive they are and, by way of illustration, it is usually said that it is possible to catch todies with a butterfly net. Alexander Wetmore tells how he shared the shelter of a banana plant with a Puerto Rican tody during a heavy downpour. The tody perched almost within reach of him. Such tameness is not unusual on remote islands where there are no mammalian predators but it is surprising for a small West Indian bird to be so fearless.

With such brilliant plumage and their fearless nature, todies would be pleasing cagebirds, but they have not been kept successfully in captivity. One that did survive in the Bronx Zoo was found to have a very high metabolic rate and to need nearly half its own weight in food each day.

class	**Aves**
order	**Coraciiformes**
family	**Todidae**
genus & species	***Todus angustirostris*** *narrow-billed tody*
	T. mexicanus *Puerto Rican tody*
	T. multicolor *Cuban tody*
	T. subulatus *broad-billed tody*
	T. todus *Jamaican tody*

Tomb bat

The name 'tomb bat' has been given to several kinds of bats belonging to two related families because they roost in tombs and pyramids in Egypt. More important than this, however, the two families offer a contrast in tails and their use.

The members of the two families both have peculiarities worth noting. The first family, Rhinopomatidae, consists of four species that are also known as mouse-tailed, rat-tailed or long-tailed bats. They are 3 in. or less in head and body length with a tail, which is almost entirely free of the very small interfemoral membrane,

of nearly the same length. These bats are greyish brown to brown, paler on the underside, with the face and rump bare of fur. The ears are large and connected by a fold of skin and each has an earlet. There is a small rounded noseleaf on the snout and a concavity on the forehead.

The second family, Emballonuridae, contains about 40 species. Head and body length is 1½ – 4 in. and they are usually grey, brown or black in colour. Some species have white markings and three types, known as ghost bats, are all white. There is no noseleaf, but the ears are connected by a fold of skin and each has an earlet. Many species have glandular

sacs on the upper surface of each wing which give out a strongly smelling red secretion. In all species the tail is short, with normally only the tip showing through the interfemoral membrane, which forms a sheath round the base of the tail. In flight the membrane is often stretched as the bat moves its legs to steer and the tail then protrudes more. The members of this family are called sheath-tailed bats or sac-winged bats, and apart from the three called ghost bats, a dozen are also known as tomb bats.

The Rhinopomatidae range from Egypt across southern Asia to Burma. The Emballonuridae are spread across the tropics in both Old and New Worlds.

Desert bats

Tomb bats roost in caves, crevices in rocks, ruins of buildings, houses and tombs, and some of the Emballonuridae roost in hollow trees, under logs, and even in large curled leaves. Except for the mouse-tailed bats, which seem to be able to hang equally well by the thumb claws on the wings as by the hindfeet, when at rest, the lives of all these bats are rather similar to those of other insectivorous bats. Tomb bats differ from other bats in their flight. The mouse-tailed bats have an undulating flight, like that of many birds. They fly between 18—30 ft above the ground in a series of glides alternating with short periods of wingbeating, which gives them an up-and-down flight. The sac-winged bats fly in the usual flittering way of small bats but with greater manoeuvrability because of the way they can adjust the interfemoral membrane, trimming it as a yachtsman would a sail.

The secretions from the glands of the sac-winged bats are probably effective in some way in bringing the sexes together. In some species males and females normally roost separately. A few have similar glands on the chin and, from what is known of other land mammals with chin glands, these probably have a sexual significance.

The mouse-tailed bats live almost entirely over deserts or dry country and it is interesting that they, like the camel, have slit-like nostrils which they can close at will. The inference seems to be that this protects them from wind-borne sand.

Storing fat

The food of both sac-winged and mouse-tailed bats is insects, especially night-flying beetles and moths. Some are thought to eat small quantities of fruit occasionally. The mouse-tailed bats and some of the sac-winged bats seasonally store fat under the skin of the abdomen. This has been taken to mean that although living in the tropics they have a regular period of extended sleep comparable to the hibernation of bats in temperate zones.

▽ *Acting big! A small tomb bat* **Taphozous saccolaimus** *takes offence at being disturbed. The prime demands of this bat are a firm surface against which to rest its body, and at least partial shade.*

P Morris

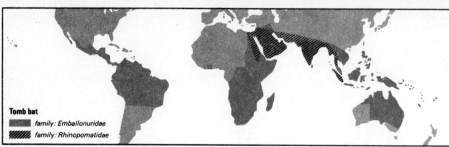

Tomb bat

▨ family: *Emballonuridae*

▧ family: *Rhinopomatidae*

family: **Emballonuridae**

family: **Rhinopomatidae**

Alan Rees: PDAI

The mystery of breeding

Too little is known of the breeding of any of these species to be able to give more than the widest generalization. Some species seem to breed throughout the year, others at the wet season, and for those living in desert or semi-desert regions the females have been found to be pregnant at various times from March to July.

Tombs and ghosts

Judging from the way bats have always been associated in folklore with darkness and death it is easy to suppose that scientists, despite their reputation for not being superstitious, should have readily accepted the name 'tomb bat'. For the bats themselves, however, a tomb or a pyramid is merely another form of cave, and caves have been their natural roosts since long before man built even a mud hut. One species, *Rhinopoma microphyllum*, seems to have been roosting in the pyramids for at least 5 000 years. There is more logic in the use of this common name for an entirely different bat. In his book 'Listening In the Dark', Donald Griffin, the celebrated student of bats, speaks of *Roussettus aegypticus*, a species of flying fox, as the tomb bat. He gives it this name because it appears in the tomb wall paintings, dating from 2 000 BC.

As if to emphasize the macabre nature of these two families of bats, some of the Emballonuridae living in tropical America are pure white or greyish-white. Appropriately they have been called ghost bats, as well as white bats, but they roost in rolled leaves not in tombs. All white bats, other than the occasional albinos, are most unusual. One hesitates to suggest what legends might have arisen had ghost bats lived and roosted in the Pharaohs' tombs.

class	**Mammalia**
order	**Chiroptera**
family	**Rhinopomatidae**
genus & species	***Rhinopoma microphyllum***
family	**Emballonuridae**
genus & species	***Taphozous perforatus*** *others*

◁△ *Not as evil-looking as its name implies. A* **Taphozous** *tomb bat of the family Rhinopomatidae. It differs noticeably from an emballonurid in having widely separated ears and no nose-flaps.*

◁ *Diagrams showing the differences between the tomb bat families (½ natural size). The top diagram is of* **T. mauritianus** *of the Emballonuridae, its most obvious characteristic being the short tail that is included within the interfemoral membrane. The pocket of skin on the throat is known as the gular sac and probably has a sexual function.*
The bottom diagram is of **R. hardwickei** *of the Rhinopomatidae, immediately recognisable by the long tail. Its fur is shorter and sparser than that of an emballonurid. These diagrams clearly show how the mammalian pentadactyl limb has been modified in the bats, for flying.*

Klaus Paysan

Tooth-carp

The tooth-carps might almost have been designed to catch the eye and hold the attention of the aquarist while inflicting the maximum perplexity on those responsible for classifying them. Some experts put about 200 species into the tooth-carp family Cyprinodontidae, others divide the family up into half-a-dozen smaller families. A third group keeps the family as one unit and divides them into two halves, the egg-bearing tooth-carps and the live-bearing tooth-carps. The last of these contains several fishes we have already dealt with, such as guppies (p 991), mollies, platys (p 1789) and swordtails. It is convenient therefore to deal now with the egg-bearing tooth-carps only.

These are all small carp-like fishes, but unlike carps they have many small comb-like teeth on the jaws and in the throat. Most tooth-carps are 2 in. long, the largest species reaching a maximum of 4 in. The upper surface of the head is flattened. The protrusible mouth is at the end of the snout and is directed slightly upwards. There are no barbels. The dorsal fin is prominent and lies behind the midline of the body; the anal fin is similar in shape and size but slightly more forward.

They live in the rivers of North and South America, the Mediterranean region, much of tropical Africa, in southern and southeast Asia and in Japan.

Rainbow hues
Tooth-carps live in the smaller streams, especially those with clear water and a fair supply of water plants with finely divided leaves. They live in very loose formations

△ *This beautiful variety of **Aphyosemion australe** has only recently been developed. Fish of this genus are found in brackish pools around the river deltas of West Africa.*

▽ *A male American flagfish. One of the few species of tooth-carp that care for their brood — the male fans the eggs and looks after the fry in a similar way to the cichlids.*

H Hansen

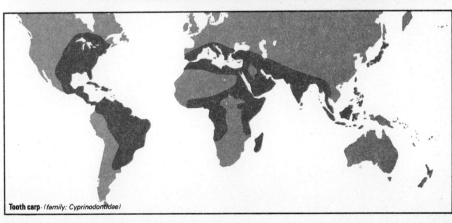

Tooth carp (family: Cyprinodontidae)

or in small groups. Shoaling in the true sense is not possible because of the way many of them swim, alternately making rapid darts forward and then staying still for a few moments with beating fins. This method of swimming enables them to dash to cover among waterweeds, so concealing their bright colours. Between them, the tooth carps show all the colours of the rainbow, with blues, reds and violet predominating. Their bodies are usually translucent or semi-translucent, and the males especially are brightly, even brilliantly coloured with spots, bars, or other markings in a variety of colours. The females, although less showy and with more subdued colours than the males, are nevertheless decorative. This is why so many of the species are popular aquarium fishes.

Keeping down mosquitoes

Tooth-carps are used by anglers as bait in some places but they also have a value in helping to control insect pests such as mosquitoes. Their food is mainly midge and mosquito larvae, small crustaceans of the type commonly called water fleas, and small worms. Some of the larger species also take the young of other fishes. They eat a small amount of plant food. Some of the tooth-carps are described as 'good jumpers' and this to an aquarist means they are liable to leap out of an aquarium and land on the floor. Species of *Rivulus*, of tropical America, are very prone to do this. In the wild state they travel short distances over the ground in wet weather and will catch insects and worms while doing so.

High and low spawners

Apart from their less lively colours the females are usually slightly smaller than the males and have smaller fins. Tooth-carps may spawn among water plants or on the bottom. The plant spawners' courtship is often a lively affair. The male flutters around the female like a butterfly or nods and dances around her, with his fins spread and colours heightened. In the bottom spawners the male swims beside the female with spread fins and the two swim to the bottom to nestle side by side. The leaf spawners lay sticky eggs on water plants, the bottom spawners bury them in the mud with a powerful flick of the tail. The details vary considerably from species to species but generally it can be said they lay up to 200 eggs in batches of 8 – 12 and spawning may last 2 – 3 weeks. With leaf spawners the eggs hatch in 6 – 14 days, or as much as 36 days in some species. Eggs of bottom spawners develop more slowly and may take 3 – 9 weeks to hatch or as much as 6 months. The baby fishes feed on protistans and on the smallest larvae of crustaceans such as water fleas. Some tooth-carps have a life span of only one year, and are therefore, logically enough, known as annuals.

▽ *A pair of **Rivulus agilis**. These fish are pronounced surface feeders, often hanging motionless near the surface waiting for insect prey. They are good jumpers, and like to lie in the sun on the leaves of water plants. The spawning period may last several weeks—in the aquarium it is advisable to remove the parents after spawning as they tend to eat the eggs.*

Few eggs, few enemies

There is little recorded information on the enemies of tooth-carps and although a percentage of them almost inevitably must be taken by fish-eating birds and other such predators, this proportion cannot be high. The fact that a spawning produces the relatively small reproduction rate of no more than 200 eggs is a clear indication of this. So also is the small amount of parental care shown. One species that does show more parental care is the American flagfish, of Florida. The female lays her eggs in a depression in the mud and the male aerates and guards them.

Looking after offspring

In a sense all bottom spawners show some sort of parental care, if only by burying the eggs. In a few the female forces the eggs into the mud, using her pelvic fins cupped together as a kind of chute which guides each egg into the hole the fins make in the mud. In other species, living in streams liable to seasonal drying, the parents may be killed off by the loss of water but the eggs lying in the mud will hatch with the first rains, which may be weeks later. These are only a few of the many different ways in which the breeding habits of tooth-carps vary. Some lay their eggs one at a time, each being fertilised separately by the male. Others lay them in batches. The female ricefish, of Japan, carries her eggs around for a time in a mucus sheath which she later rubs off on a water plant. The Cuban killie female lays relatively large eggs which remain for a while in a bunch of half a dozen, hanging from her genital opening by a slender thread of mucus. Finally this catches in a water plant and sticks to it. Meanwhile the eggs have had some protection from being attached to the parent while undergoing the early stages of development. So spawning among tooth-carps is not such a haphazard process as it may seem at first sight.

Even the fertilisation is not as random as would appear. Fish eggs, in many species, including tooth-carps, are at first slightly flattened. Once laid, the egg's capsule, or outer covering, becomes spherical and sucks in, through a tiny opening called the micropyle, a small amount of the water which has just been charged with the male's milt.

H Hansen

class	**Pisces**
order	**Atheriniformes**
family	**Cyprinodontidae**
genera & species	***Cyprinodon variegatus*** sheepshead top minnow ***Cubanichthys cubensis*** Cuban killie ***Fundulus heteroclitus*** zebra killie ***F. diaphanus*** banded killifish ***Jordanella floridae*** American flagfish ***Oryzias latipes*** ricefish ***Rivulus cylindraceus*** green rivulus others

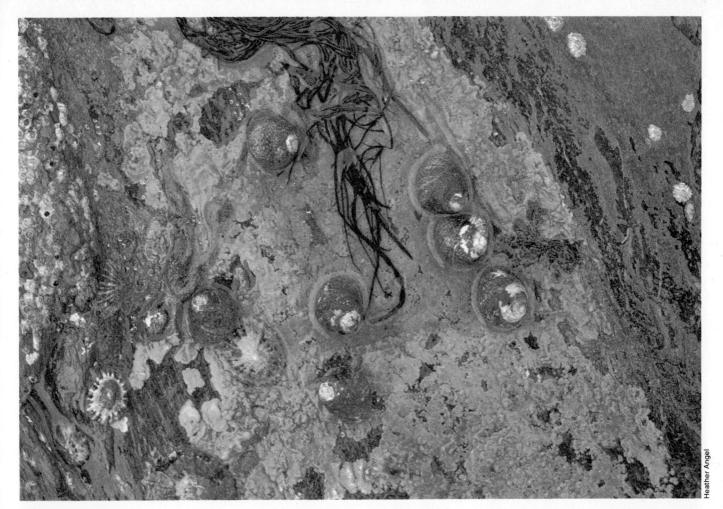

Topshell

Topshells are periwinkles with a difference. They are more cone-shaped and more decorative and the larger kinds figure prominently in the cabinets of shell collectors. They are named for their resemblance to the whip tops of the 19th century that finally went out of fashion as children's toys in the first decade of this century. Not only have they the colours and shape of the whip top but the apex of the shell, through being worn, is silvery and looks like the bright metal peg on which the top spun.

They range from $\frac{1}{25}$ to 6 in. across the base and the lower part of the shell is usually marked with distinct spiral ridges or oblique bands of colour. Their ornate appearance is reflected in some of their common names such as the painted, pearly and grey topshells of European seas, and the brick-red topshell of the Pacific coast of North America. The painted topshell is pink or yellow, flecked with crimson or red-brown. It is 1 in. high and slightly less across the base. The grey topshell is pale grey to yellow with oblique streaks of dark purple. It is also called the silver Tommy, from the silvery appearance of its worn upper surface. The head of the mollusc inside bears a pair of sensory tentacles which are organs of touch and

taste, and each has an eye near its base. There are two flattened fleshy processes between the tentacles. Along the sides of the foot are 3–6 pairs of longer tentacles and at the rear of the foot is a circular cover, or operculum, which closes the entrance to the shell when the mollusc withdraws into it. In fact it is pulled so far in when the animal retracts that it is no longer visible.

There are over 50 genera of topshells. Many species are found between tidemarks but most of them live offshore and down to depths of 600 ft. They are most numerous in tropical and subtropical seas.

Progress by reduction

Topshells are found on rocks or on coral rather than sandy or muddy shores because silt or mud tends to clog their gills. They are also found in rock pools. William J Dakin has described how 'no matter where you wander over the rocky flats of the ocean beaches from Queensland to Western Australia you will find myriads of these little shells'. Some species live in quiet bays, and the empty shells of those living below low tide mark are often thrown up on beaches.

They belong to the most primitive group of prosobranch gastropods, which generally have two auricles to the heart, two gills, two kidneys and no operculum. The evolution of higher prosobranchs led to the acquisition of an operculum and the loss of one kidney, one gill, and one auricle.

△ *Grey top shells exposed at low water.*

The topshells have gone only part of the way along this evolutionary line, as they have two auricles and two kidneys but only one gill, which lies in the shelter of the shell, in the mantle cavity.

By-passing the larva

In primitive gastropods, such as the grey topshell, and also in bivalves, the eggs are fertilised after being shed into the sea. Simple trochophore larvae hatch from them, each larva swimming by means of a girdle of cilia. From these trochophores shelled larvae, veligers, soon develop, with ciliated lobes that can be protruded from the shell for swimming and for feeding. In others, such as the painted topshell which is in several ways more advanced, the eggs are laid in gelatinous ribbons and the young eventually emerge as miniature, creeping adults, having been nourished in the meantime by a large yolk. Before these young snails emerge, however, they pass through the veliger larva stage and these can be seen rotating inside their capsules. In some species a rise of temperature provides enough stimulus to set off spawning. For others this is not enough, they require an individual of the opposite sex to be in the vicinity. This latter condition is probably the more effective as there is more chance of fertilisation taking place and thus less wastage of eggs and sperm. These are released through one of the two kidneys, the eggs being laid through the right kidney.

Tops of buttons

One of the largest topshells, measuring up to 5 or 6 in. across the base, is the button shell of the shallow waters of the Great Barrier Reef, the northern Australian coasts and the Indo-Pacific. Its shell, when not encrusted with marine organisms, such as seaweeds and sea-firs, is white marked with wavy red-brown bands and, because of its mother-of-pearl interior, is collected for the manufacture of buttons. Several kinds of mollusc shell are used for this purpose, but some of those made from 'trocas', to use the commercial name, are recognizable by a purplish crimson mark on the back. Button shells are gathered by wading, or skin-diving to depths of about 36 ft. The boats in which they are collected have smoke houses for drying and smoking the meat, most of which is sent to the Orient. Japan was the principal buyer of shells before the war and she also then supplied many of the divers. Today most of the shells go to America and the diving off Australia is now largely carried on by Torres Straits islanders. The exports of shell from Australia in 1955–56 amounted to 938 tons, worth £545 640 (Australian). Papua and New Guinea exported troca shells to about the same value, £A358 227. The industry is controlled by licence and collected shells must be at least 2½ in. across the base—a size corresponding more or less to the onset of maturity at an age of about two years.

phylum	**Mollusca**
class	**Gastropoda**
subclass	**Prosobranchia**
order	**Archaeogastropoda**
family	**Trochidae**
genera & species	***Astraea inaequalis*** brick-red topshell ***Calliostoma annulatum*** ring topshell ***C. zizyphinum*** painted topshell ***Gibbula cineraria*** grey topshell ***Trochus niloticus*** button topshell others

△ *On the move: a painted topshell flails its head tentacles as it searches for food. Topshells browse on a wide variety of plants ranging from the film of diatoms that often covers rocks, to quite large fucoid seaweeds. Related to limpets, topshells are characterised by having additional sensory tentacles on the sides of the foot. This specimen is shown creeping along a rock on which there is a calcareous tube of the worm* **Pomatoceros** *and numerous tubes of* **Spirorbis** *worms. The painted topshell lives in deepwater in the North Sea, Atlantic and Mediterranean.*

▽ *A group of flat topshells,* **Gibbula umbilicalis**, *identified by their purple stripes.*

Torrent duck

The torrent ducks of South America differ from other ducks in several ways, especially in their habit of living in fast-flowing mountain streams. Their appearance and behaviour, also, are very different from other ducks. There is one species, which is divided by different writers into three or six geographically separate subspecies. Torrent ducks have slender bodies with long, stiff tails and are about the same size as a teal (p 2378), being 17 in. long. Both sexes bear horny spurs, about ½ in. long, on the 'elbows'. Their function is unknown: they do not, like other birds that have them, seem to use them for fighting. The plumage is very distinctive, varying slightly between the subspecies. The male has a white head and neck with bold black lines running over the head and down the neck. The feathers of the back are long with black centres and white edges, giving a streaked effect. There is a brilliant green speculum edged with white on the wings, as in mallards. The underparts are greyish or brown, the bill bright red and the legs dull red. The female is unusually coloured with a cinnamon red chin, throat and underparts, a greyish back streaked with black and a speculum similar to the male's.

Torrent ducks range from northern Venezuela to Tierra del Fuego but they are confined to a relatively narrow stretch of country on each side of the Andes.

Noel Simon

Heedless of the swirling and pounding white surf of the surrounding waters, a torrent duck rests calmly on a large boulder. They seldom fly and never stray far from rapid-flowing streams.

Wary stream dwellers

The peculiar habitat of the torrent ducks is the cold, rapid-flowing streams coming down the Andes. The ducks are never seen far from the banks of these streams and are confined to watercourses where there are rapids and waterfalls and where boulders stand out of the water. They seldom fly, and then they do little more than fly along the course of the stream. The streams can be as narrow as 6 ft and still be acceptable to the ducks. In these conditions other waterbirds would be instantly swept away but the torrent ducks swim up and down with little apparent effort, keeping the body submerged. In the most rapid currents they move upstream by pattering over the surface with wings beating. Waterfalls are usually negotiated by flight but if in danger torrent ducks will swim over the top and drop to the lower level.

Apart from the inaccessibility of their habitat, torrent ducks have been very difficult to study because of their extreme wariness. At the slightest disturbance they slip into the water, where the black and white or grey upper plumage makes them difficult to spot, and usually swim a short distance upstream then dive and float downstream or hide under a waterfall.

Diving for food

Torrent ducks eat small water animals such as caddis fly larvae, snails and small fish, which they pick from stones on the stream bed with their soft, rubbery bills. Floating animals are sometimes picked out of the water as they are swept past, but more usually the ducks forage from a particular rock from which they dive repeatedly, submerging for about 15 seconds then reappearing at the same spot.

Few nests found

Although it is comparatively easy to spot torrent ducks by approaching their stream carefully, finding their nests has proved to be very difficult; there are very few records of them. They are placed very close to the stream, hidden under overhanging ledges or among vegetation. One was found in the abandoned burrow of a kingfisher.

Finding nests is made difficult by the low population density of torrent ducks—usually less than one pair per mile. Unlike other ducks, they are never gregarious, and it is thought that they may pair for life as the male never assumes an eclipse plumage. He also appears to assist in caring for the brood. In the courtship display the pair swim around each other, snapping at the air with their bills and rearing up vertically. The clutch varies from 2 to 5 buff coloured eggs. These are very large, 2½ by 1¾ in. as compared to the 2 by 1¾ in. of teal eggs. It has been suggested that the size of the eggs implies that the chicks are well developed when they hatch and so are able to cope with life in fast-flowing water from an early age.

Designed for currents

Torrent ducks are very well adapted for life in the seemingly dangerous world of waterfalls and rapids. It is possible that they exploit the life that exists in the swirling, well-oxygenated water. It is not known how they manage to swim so well against the current but it has been suggested that their long stiff tails are used for manoeuvring underwater. They are, however, known to be used as props when climbing boulders or steep banks, in the same way as a woodpecker uses its tail. Torrent ducks are not the only ducks living in this type of habitat. The blue duck *Hymenolaimus malacorhynchos* of New Zealand also lives in mountain torrents, although it sometimes strays onto lakes or estuaries. It has a bluish-grey plumage and the bill bears a soft membrane hanging from the side. Its feeding habits are similar to those of the torrent duck but the blue duck is very tame and as a result is now rather rare.

class	**Aves**
order	**Anseriformes**
family	**Anatidae**
genus & species	*Merganetta armata*

2381

Tortoise

Tortoises are well known for their slowness of movement and for their long life span. They live longer than any other animal today; and they are about the most heavily armoured. There is a difference between American and British usage. In the United States the name 'tortoise' is used only for land-living chelonians belonging to the family Testudinidae. In British usage some water-living chelonians, such as the European pond tortoise, are also given the common name of tortoise.

There are about 40 land tortoises, the best known of which are the so-called garden tortoises and the giant tortoises. Since the way of life of all of them is much the same, most attention will be given here to the Iberian or Algerian tortoise and the Greek or Hermann's tortoise, both garden tortoises. They have high domed shells, up to 1 ft long. The legs are covered with hard scales which often have bony cores and the five toes on the forefoot and the four on the hindfoot all have stout claws. When disturbed a tortoise pulls its head and limbs into the shelter of the bony box covered with horn which is usually spoken of as its shell. The head is completely withdrawn. The front legs are pulled back to make the elbows meet in the middle, protecting the entrance with their scaly skin. The hindlegs and tail are similarly withdrawn, the soles of the hindfeet sealing the entrance.

Tortoises live in tropical and subtropical regions. The Iberian or Algerian tortoise is found in northwest Africa and Spain, the Balkans, Iraq and Persia. The Greek tortoise ranges from southern France through parts of Italy to the Balkans. The star tortoise of southern Asia has pale star-shaped markings on its shell. The gopher tortoises of the southern United States get their name from the French **gaufre**, a honeycomb, an allusion to their burrowing. There are other land tortoises in southern Asia, Africa, Madagascar and other islands of the Indian Ocean, South America and the Galapagos Islands.

▷ Galapagos giant tortoises: some of the few remaining members of a species once numerous enough to give its name to the islands but numbers are now greatly diminished. In the 19th century they were easy prey for the crews of passing ships, and their hardiness enabled them to be kept on board as a live source of meat.

ES Hobson

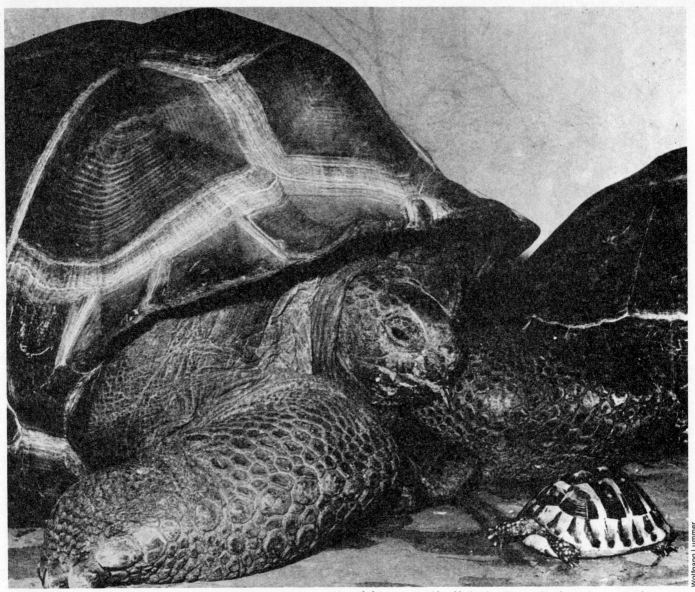

△ *Tortoises are widespread in tropical and subtropical regions of the world, and they vary considerably in size. Here a Greek tortoise seems to be retreating into its shell as the scaly front legs and head of an Indian Ocean giant tower above it.*

The warmer, the faster

Tortoises live in sandy places or among rocks or in woodlands. They are active by day and generally slow in their movements, yet they can at times reach a speed of 2 mph over short distances. This may be slow compared with the speed of most quadrupeds but it is nearly the walking speed of a man and is faster than we normally consider tortoises' speed. The behaviour of a tortoise is geared to the temperature of the surrounding air. Its movements are faster in warmer temperatures but like other reptiles it is intolerent of the higher air temperatures. Tortoises spend some time every day basking. In temperate latitudes garden tortoises hibernate from October to March, fasting for a while prior to digging themselves into soft earth or under dead vegetation.

Seedlings a favourite meal

It was once widely believed that the smaller tortoises fed on insects and slugs and for this reason people, in England at least, bought tortoises to keep in their gardens. The idea is not yet wholly dead. It may be that a garden tortoise will sometimes eat the smaller garden vermin, but anyone who has seen a tortoise travel along a row of seedlings just showing through the ground will need little convincing that tortoises are wholly or almost exclusively vegetarian, eating low growing vegetation such as seedlings, succulent leaves, flowers and fallen fruits, and occasionally insects.

Battering ram courtship

Males and females look alike but in most species there is some small difference in shape. In Hermann's tortoise, for example, the plastron, or underside of the shell, is flat in the female, concave in the male. In the Iberian tortoise the tail shield is flat in the female, curved in the male. Another sign is that a male in breeding condition butts the female in the flank, at the same time hissing slightly. Male garden tortoises, when there is no female around, will butt the shoes of people sitting in the garden or the legs of garden chairs. The female lays 4–12 whitish spherical eggs, each 1½ in. diameter, in a hole which she digs in soft ground. The eggs hatch 3–4 months later.

Man the enemy today . . .

The solid box of bone with its horny covering and the tortoise's habit of withdrawing into this fortress at the slightest disturbance, seem the best possible protection against enemies. The lammergeier (p 1275) is a traditional enemy, flying to some height with a tortoise and then letting it drop to the ground to crack its shell. Rats attack and eat tortoises. Apart from these the natural enemies must be limited. On the other hand, tortoises are probably very vulnerable to the elements, especially to such catastrophes as grass and woodland fires. After a grass fire the number of dead tortoises of all sizes, and especially the small ones, gives an indication of how numerous these animals can be in places where normally little is seen of them. The greatest danger today is the trade in tortoises for pets. Once a tortoise has been bought and installed in a garden it will be treated with the greatest care. The method of packing them for transport has meant, however, that in recent years there has been a hideously high mortality between their being collected, mainly in North Africa, and their reaching the dealers.

Anthony Bannister: NHPA

△ *A leopard tortoise* **Testudo pardalis** *about to enjoy a refreshing mouthful of cactus.*
▽ *Almost impregnable, a Texas tortoise with head drawn in straight between tucked legs.*

John Tashjian

... and in the past

The four species of gopher tortoises, which may be up to 13 in. long, have also suffered from the pet trade. Two, the Texas tortoise and the desert tortoise, are now protected by law but the Mexican is very rare and may be extinct. The giant tortoises which live on the islands of the Galapagos and on islands in the Indian Ocean have also suffered in numbers, but in a different way. The largest of them have reached nearly 5 ft long, stood 2½ ft high and weighed 200 – 300 lb. Those of the Galapagos especially were taken by the crews of whalers, sealers and buccaneers for fresh meat. Between 1811 and 1844, a mere 105 whalers took 15 000. The giant tortoises of the Indian Ocean suffered even more, and in recent years a population on Aldabra Island was threatened through a proposal by the British Ministry of Defence to make the island an air staging post.

A ripe old age

Keeping tortoises as pets has been the only means we have of estimating how long they can live. The first of the 'famous' pets was the tortoise belonging to Archbishop Laud. It lived in the gardens of Lambeth Palace in London and its shell is still preserved in the Palace, with two labels that contradict each other. One says the tortoise lived there from 1633 to 1753, the other gives the year of its death as 1730. The bishops of Peterborough also had a pet tortoise which has been credited with living 220 years. Again the records are conflicting; all we can say is that it may have lived 62 years (1757-1819) or 92 years (1747-1839). Gilbert White's tortoise 'Timothy' lived for at least 54 years.

The longest authentic record we have is for one of the giant tortoises, Marion's tortoise. It was taken to Mauritius, when full grown, by Marion de Fresne in 1766. In 1810 the British captured the island and the tortoise continued to live in the artillery barracks until 1918. It was, therefore, at least 152 years old, and probably 180 years or even more. Another famous giant is the Tonga tortoise, presented by Captain James Cook in 1774, when it was already 'a considerably age'. In 1951 it was blind in one eye, had survived two bush fires, been kicked by a horse and run over by a dray. If still alive now (1970) it will be over 200 years old. There is some doubt about this tortoise, largely because in Tonga the records are oral, not written, but there seems no reason why the present tortoise should not be the same as the one Captain Cook handed over.

class	**Reptilia**
order	**Chelonia**
family	**Testudinidae**
genera & species	***Gopherus agassizi*** *desert gopher tortoise*
	G. berlandieri *Texas*
	G. flavomarginatus *Mexican*
	Testudo elephantopus *Galapagos giant*
	T. gigantea *Indian Ocean giant*
	T. graeca *Iberian or Algerian*
	T. hermanni *Greek, others*

Toucan

The huge, bizarre bills of the toucans are rivalled only by those of the hornbills (p 1106). They may even be as long and bulky as the rest of the bird. The toucan family consists of about 37 species of large birds, up to 24 in. long, with brightly coloured plumage. The bill is also distinctively coloured but lacks the helmet-like outgrowth typical of the hornbills. The legs are quite strong and on each foot the two toes face in opposite directions. The tail is usually fairly long and the wings short and rounded.

The largest toucans are those in the genus **Rhamphastos**, such as the rainbow-billed toucan. This toucan is mainly black with a green gloss but there is a patch of white just above the tail and red on the underparts and there is also some yellow on the cheeks and throat. The colour of the bill varies in different individuals and contains all the colours of the rainbow, except violet, and is black at the base. Related toucans are also mainly black with varying patches of yellow, white and red on the throat and at the base of the tail feathers.

The araçaris make up a group of small toucans. The collared araçari is mainly greenish-black with a black head and neck and bold patches of red and yellow on the underparts. The eyes are surrounded by rings of naked red skin. The lower half of the bill is black and the upper half greyish-yellow with serrations on the edges. The toucanets form a third group with mainly green plumage.

The toucans are confined to the tropical parts of the American continents, the similar but unrelated hornbills being confined to the Old World. Toucans range from Mexico to Argentina.

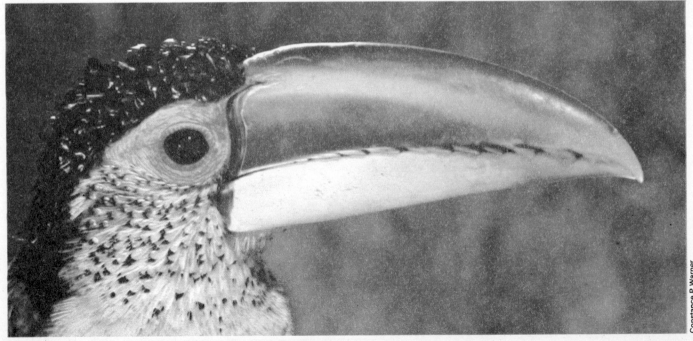

billed toucans have been seen nesting in holes $3\frac{1}{4}$ in. in diameter, only just large enough for them to squeeze into. This species brings fresh leaves to line the nest and replaces them when they wither.

Because the nest hole is usually high in a tree, almost inaccessible and obscured from view by foliage, few details are known about the nesting habits of toucans. Alexander Skutch records how a group of six collared araçaris roosted in one hole but once eggs were laid in it only one of the six slept there. After the chicks hatched, however, all six araçaris roosted with them and helped feed them. Presumably the group consisted of two adults and four juveniles, perhaps from a previous brood, which were banished from the hole during the incubation period.

The clutch consists of 2—4 white eggs which are incubated by both parents. The eggs are often left uncovered for up to one hour. Those of the smaller toucans hatch in 16 days. The chicks are blind and naked at first and develop slowly, taking 6—7 weeks to fledge.

Mystery of the freak bill

The large bill of the toucan is a puzzle although it is not as ungainly as it first seems. The horny outer layer is supported by a network of bony filaments which make it extremely light but very strong. As to its function, however, almost every possible suggestion has been made. One of the earliest ideas was that it was 'an admirable contrivance of nature to increase the delicacy of smell'. There is no evidence at all for this strange idea but neither is there any evidence to support the theory that the bill is used as a weapon. A toucan can certainly deliver a painful peck, but so can a parrot or even a crow, which have much smaller bills.

In general the bills of birds are adapted for their particular method of feeding; hooked for flesheaters, conical for seedeaters and so on, and unusual bills such as those of spoonbills, crossbills and avocets can be shown to be adapted to certain feeding habits. But it is difficult to see how the massive bill of the toucan is of particular advantage in eating fruit. A long bill is useful for reaching distant fruit but it need not be so bulky. It may be that the toucan's bill has the same function as a crest or ruff, that is as an ornament to function as a signal either in aggressive or courtship displays. Toucans sometimes spar and wrestle with their bills and this may be a form of ritualised fighting. Until more observations are made on their habits it is wise not to speculate too freely.

△ Panamanian pair in a jungle setting: the chestnut-mandibled toucan **Ramphastos swainsonii** *is noted for its penetrating call, that has been described as a loud, yelping, gull-like 'kee-you tedick-tedick-tedick'.*

◁ Top-heavy toucanet? For all its massive size the toucan's bill is very light. It is mainly filled with air with an inner mass of delicate supporting tissue. The whole bill is ensheathed by a thin shell which gives it strength. This curly-crested toucanet **Pteroglossus beauharnaesii** *is one of the most aberrant and colourful of the family: its crest appears to be made of strips of isinglass.*

Roosting together

Toucans are exclusively woodland birds and are found only in forests, where they are surprisingly inconspicuous, despite their large size and bold colouring. Once in flight, however, their silhouettes are unmistakable and if they utter their monotonous calls they can be heard over long distances. Living in small flocks of about a dozen birds, toucans have been found roosting with araçaris in holes in trees, such as old woodpecker holes. Each group has several roosting places, moving from one to another if disturbed. The tail is jointed to fold over the back and save space when roosting.

Apart from the bizarre charm of their huge bills toucans are delightful birds; they are readily tamed and are inquisitive and playful. The toucanets are good mimics as well. They delight in bathing and make use of the pools of water that collect where branches join tree trunks.

Mixed bill of fare

Fruit forms the major part of the toucans' diet. Small fruits and berries are plucked and eaten whole while larger fruits have sections torn out. The long bill is useful for reaching out for fruit, which is held in the tip of the bill and passed to the mouth with an upward flick of the head. The diet of fruit is supplemented with insects, such as flying termites, spiders and occasional lizards and the nestlings of birds.

Overcrowded dormitory

The various toucan species when nesting are unable to do more than enlarge existing holes where the wood is rotten. Rainbow-

class	**Aves**
order	**Piciformes**
family	**Ramphastidae**
genera & species	*Aulacorhynchus caeruleogularis* blue-throated toucanet *Pteroglossus torquatus* collared araçari *Ramphastos sulfuratus* rainbow billed toucan others

△ *Blue in the face: the dazzling head and shoulders of a male Temminck's tragopan.*

▽ *One of the few: attempts are being made in Britain to breed the rare Cabot's tragopan.*

Tragopan

The five tragopans or horned pheasants are among the most brilliantly coloured pheasants. In all, the bill is short, the wings rounded and the tail comparatively short, being less than the wing length. The males bear two fleshy horns and a bib-like wattle on the throat which are displayed during courtship. The plumage of the males of four species is speckled with white eyespots, each surrounded by a black border. In the fifth, Cabot's tragopan, the eyespots, or ocelli, are buff standing out against the black, brown and red upperparts. The underparts are buff. The head is black and red with a large yellow patch of bare skin around the eye. The satyr tragopan is mainly crimson-red with ocelli both above and below. The head is black with a red crown. The western tragopan has a similar pattern of ocelli and has a red head and neck with black markings but the body is mainly grey. Blyth's tragopan is rather similar with a brown back and yellow naked skin on the face. Temminck's tragopan has blue skin on the face and the body is brownish red with ocelli on the upperparts and large spots underneath where each feather is grey with a red border. Female tragopans have, by comparison, dull plumage with patterns of black, brown and grey.

Tragopans originally ranged along the Himalayas from western Pakistan to Burma and into China as far as Fukien. The western tragopan once inhabited the Indus valley in West Pakistan and Kashmir and the satyr tragopan continued along the southern side of the Himalayas to East Pakistan and Burma. Temminck's tragopan ranges from eastern India and Burma far into central China and Cabot's tragopan is found in eastern China, in the provinces of Kwansi and Fukien. Most tragopans are now very rare and live in scattered pockets over their former ranges.

Highland foresters

The ranges of the tragopans indicate their preference for mountainous forests. They live at altitudes between 3 000 and 12 000 ft in the wet, cool forests along the lower slopes of the Himalayas and the mountains of China. In the winter months the tragopans live at lower altitudes in mixed evergreen forests then migrate to higher levels near the treeline dominated by rhododendrons and birch. They live singly or in pairs, hiding among the foliage and giving themselves away only by their quavering calls.

Although very wary and shy in the wild, tragopans become tame in captivity, even feeding from the hand. In the wild, tragopans feed on berries, seeds, leaves, shoots and insects.

Goat's horns and bibs

The satyr tragopan gets its name from the goat-like horns borne by the male. Other

male tragopans also possess these horns, however, as well as a lappet or wattle on the throat. Both horns and lappet are usually tucked out of sight but during the breeding season they are erected. The blue horns rise 2–3 in. high and the lappet, also blue, is spread like a bib. During courtship the male first performs the actions common to the courtship of all pheasants. He circles the female with one wing lowered and the other slightly raised so that he appears to be leaning towards her. Having shown off his plumage to the best advantage he rushes towards the female with horns and lappet spread then suddenly stops with plumage fluffed and wings partly spread. The final phase is for the head to be shaken and the horns and lappet to be raised and spread to their full extent. This dazzling display is all over in a few seconds, the plumage flattened, horns and lappet tucked away.

Tragopans are more at home in trees than other pheasants and often nest in them, using the abandoned nest of a crow or other large bird, perhaps 40 ft up. The female lines the nest with freshly plucked twigs and leaves and lays 3–4 eggs. These hatch in 28–30 days and the newly hatched chicks are so well developed that they can fly up to roost off the ground after a few days.

Saved from extinction

Many pheasants and their relatives face extinction because of the spread of human settlement into their once almost impenetrable forest habitat. This has resulted in excessive hunting and the cutting down of the forests. Three tragopans are, however, on the danger list. The western tragopan has not been encountered for some years. Blyth's tragopan, of which there are two subspecies, lives in very remote country, and so may be safe for a while, but the typical race is known to be rare. Cabot's tragopan first brought to the attention of the western world by that great discoverer of animals, Pere David, is also very rare.

Although it seems very likely that these tragopans will eventually become extinct as truly wild birds there is a good chance that they will not completely disappear. Other pheasants have been bred in captivity for a long time and aviculturalists have succeeded in breeding most species. Two of the endangered tragopans are also rare in captivity but a stock of Cabot's tragopan has been built up in the Ornamental Pheasant Trust in England and it is hoped that some will be liberated to form a free population in the same way as the ne-ne has been reintroduced to Hawaii (p 1042).

class	**Aves**
order	**Galliformes**
family	**Phasianidae**
genus & species	***Tragopan blythi*** Blyth's tragopan
	T. caboti Cabot's tragopan
	T. melanocephalus *western tragopan*
	T. satyri *satyr tragopan*
	T. temmincki *Temminck's tragopan*

Black hairy monster **Pachylomerides nitidularis** *waits at its doorstep for prey.*

JAL Cooke

Trapdoor spider

The trapdoor spiders are related to the large hairy bird-eating spiders that are sometimes wrongly called tarantulas (p 2366). Instead of being hunters like the bird-eating spiders, trapdoor spiders have specialized in a remarkable way and have brought the building of a secure retreat, using the crafts of spinner and builder, to a fine art.

Trapdoor spiders are an inch or more long in the body with relatively short legs as compared with the bird-eating spiders. The bristles or 'hairs' on the body and legs are short, inconspicuous, and often sparse. The spiders themselves are mainly dull in colour, usually some shade of brown. Their most characteristic features are the large jaws, each with a long fang, and the row of horny teeth along the underside of them.

The true trapdoor spiders live in tropical and subtropical countries but related species, known sometimes as trapdoor spiders, but more correctly called purse-web spiders in America, are found in temperate latitudes.

▽ *In her lady's chamber: silk-lined tunnel of* **Bothriocyrtum californicum** *in cross section.*

Lynwood Chace

▽ *Seen in action:* **Cteniza caementaria** *seizes a millipede, paralyses it and retreats.*

FGH Allen

Life in a closed box

Trapdoor spiders dig a shaft in the ground which may be as much as 1 ft deep and 1−1½ in. diameter. The teeth on the underside of the jaw as well as the fangs are used to loosen soil and then to grip it and carry it away. The walls of the shaft are made firm by soil reinforced with silk, so when completed the shaft is lined with a continuous tube of silk. The entrance is secured with a trapdoor made of layers of silk and soil which form a circular, solid lid. This is coated on the outside with moss or any other readily available plant matter. Thus, when completed and in position, the trapdoor is beautifully camouflaged. Inside the lid are two holes into which the spider can fix its feet to hold the door tight down to keep out intruders. At one point there is a silken hinge and on the outside, above the hinge, there is sometimes a ridge which acts like a counterpoise.

There is nothing especially remarkable about the spider burrowing or lining the shaft with silk. Several kinds of other spiders dig in the ground and line their tunnels with silk. The masterpiece of construction is the lid or trapdoor. In some species it is toothed to give an exact fit. WS Bristowe has described a species of *Nemesia*, in Majorca, which hardens the rim of the door with cement from its mouth (or jaws) then shapes it into teeth with its fangs. The rim of the shaft is treated in the same way, but reinforced with earth. When the trapdoor is pulled down, the teeth on the lid fit between the teeth on the shaft rim. The spider is fastidious also in the material it uses. 'Only fine earth was employed, the gritty particles were held in the chelicerae (jaws) and then sharply flicked away with the palps and front legs.'

Surreptitious feeding

A hungry trapdoor spider must leave its retreat to forage. Some people say it raises the lid of its burrow slightly and watches through the crack for a passing insect. Then it lets the lid spring up, rushes out and pounces, paralysing its prey with poison from its fangs and, holding it, retreats backwards into its burrow, pulling down the trapdoor after it. Other writers say it hunts at night, but there is little information on the way trapdoor spiders feed. The poison is not dangerous to people although some species can give a painful bite; the advice given to anyone bitten by Australian trapdoor spiders is to treat their bites with as much respect as snakebites.

Underground nursery

Small, secretive animals are especially hard to study and their breeding habits particularly tend to remain unknown. The best that can be said of trapdoor spiders is that the females lay their eggs in their burrow, enclosed in a silken cocoon fixed to the wall of the shaft. The young ones stay with the mother until they are 8 months old.

Why build a trapdoor?

In fashioning such an ingenious trapdoor the spider ensures that its retreat is not filled in with dust and vegetable rubbish. It is a guard also against changes in air temperatures and heavy rain. Most of all, however, the trapdoor seems to be a protection from enemies, particularly from their main predator, the hunting wasp.

Purse-web spider

Not all trapdoor spiders use the elaborate methods described here. The lid, for example, may be paper-thin or it may be as thick as cork; it may be merely a flat circular lid or it may be elaborately scalloped or toothed. The shaft may be of varying degrees of perfection. The retreats of some of the less skilled trapdoor spiders come very near to those of the purse-web spiders, which is one reason why the latter are sometimes called trapdoor spiders. One purse-web spider *Atypus affinis*, of the family Atypidae, lives in Western Europe, from the British Isles to Denmark and Hungary and southwards into Algeria. It digs a more or less horizontal tunnel in a bank, up to 1 ft long and about ½ in. diameter. In this is a long silken bag with an inch or so lying free beyond the entrance to the tunnel. The bag is sealed at both ends and the spider inside gets its food without ever coming out. When an insect walks over the free end the spider runs to the spot and pushes its fangs through the silk to hold its victim. Then, using one jaw to hold the prey, it cuts a slit in the silk with the row of teeth along the underside of the other jaw. The fang of this jaw then holds the victim while the other jaw cuts a parallel slit close to the first. The prey is then pulled in, carried down into the tube and secured with silk threads. The spider then goes back and repairs the slits, after which it can return to eat its prey.

The male, ⅓ in. long, as against the ½in.-long female, courts her by tapping on the free end of her silken bag. If the signs are favourable he enters and mates with her. This happens during September−October but her 100−150 eggs are not laid until the following June−August, the young hatching in August and September. They remain with the mother until the following March or April. A period of 18 months elapses between mating and the time when the spiderlings leave home.

▽ *Primitive spider* **Liphistius batuensis,** *suborder Liphistiomorphae, outside her home in the Batu Caves, Malaya. The radiating lines spun by the trapdoor spider are ingenious trip lines for prey. Compare the thin pliable door of this spider's home with the thick 'cork' doors on the previous page.*

phylum	**Arthropoda**
class	**Arachnida**
order	**Araneae**
suborder	**Orthognatha**
family	**Ctenizidae**
genus & species	***Cteniza californica*** *American trapdoor spider*
family	**Barychelidae**
genus & species	***Blakistonia aurea*** *Australian trapdoor spider others*

Tree duck

The tree ducks, also known as whistling ducks, are goose-like waterfowl related to the swans (p 2328), the link being the Coscoroba swan. They are like the swans in much of their behaviour and differ from other ducks in their anatomy. Whistling duck is perhaps a better name for them because another group of ducks, the perching ducks, which includes the wood and mandarin ducks, spend more of their time in trees. The name whistling duck is derived from their whistling cries.

Tree ducks are about 17 in. long, with long necks, held upright, and short tails. The legs are fairly long and the feet are large. Like that of a swan, the bill has a hooked nail on the tip. The plumage is similar in both sexes.

The eight species of tree duck are found in tropical and subtropical parts of the Old and New Worlds. The white-faced tree duck is found on both sides of the Atlantic Ocean: in America from Costa Rica to northern Argentina and in Africa from the southern borders of the Sahara to the Transvaal and Madagascar. The head and neck are black with white on the face and throat. The back and breast are chestnut, the flanks finely striped with black and white and the underparts black. The fulvous tree duck has a rather similar distribution, ranging from California to northern Argentina, throughout most of eastern Africa, Madagascar and India. It is light brown with a darker back and the flank feathers form pale stripes. The wandering tree duck is darker, and ranges from the Philippines and Sumatra to Australia. The plumed tree duck, with greatly elongated flank feathers, is another inhabitant of Australia and the smallest is the Indian tree duck of India, southern China and southeast Asia.

White-faced tree ducks scuttle for water, encouraged by elephant and attendant egrets.

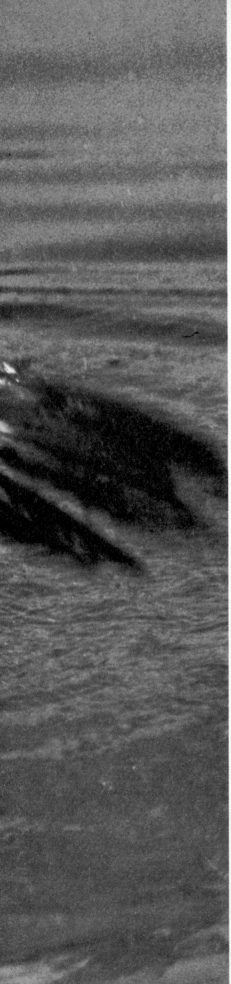

Poor sport

Although so widely distributed, the occurrence of two species on both sides of the Atlantic is most unusual. The habits of the tree duck are not particularly well-known because it is most active at night. The main stimulus to research on wildfowl has usually been their importance in sport, but tree ducks do not provide good sport—so no research. They fly slowly, often circling around the hunters and the temptation to other large bird. Unlike other ducks the nest is not lined with down.

The partners of a pair remain faithful to each other, but whereas in other ducks the male has little to do with the nesting, the male tree duck at least shares the incubation, and the two preen each other, always a sign of a close bond between a pair. There are 6—12 eggs in a clutch and they are incubated for 28—30 days. The male also helps in guarding the chicks.

◁ *White-faced tree duck bathing.* △*Bill adapted for stripping grass seeds—*Dendrocygna eytoni.

shoot at such easy targets is lessened even more by the taste of their flesh; it is not very palatable. Indeed, that of the Indian tree duck is particularly unpleasant.

For most of the year tree ducks live in flocks on rivers, swamps or pools. Many rest during the day in the cover of the swamps but some, such as the black-billed tree duck, often perch in trees. Their voices are most un-ducklike—shrill whistles that can be heard as they fly overhead or at night when they are feeding. In the tropics tree ducks move only short distances in search of food but populations of the same species at higher latitudes migrate short distances. The American population of the red-billed tree duck, which has a striking black belly and white flanks, migrates to Mexico.

Crop eater

Tree ducks are mainly vegetarian, feeding on land or diving to collect food from the bottom of shallow water. Some damage crops, and the red-billed tree duck is known in the United States as the cornfield duck because of its attacks on corn, or maize. The ducks alight on the stalks, strip the husks and eat the grains from the cob. The black-billed tree duck often feeds on the fruit of the royal palm, settling itself on the uppermost fronds.

Unlined nests

Tree ducks nest in a variety of sites, members of the same species using the sites according to circumstances. The nests are usually on the ground, hidden among reeds or grass, which are bent over to conceal them. Trees and bushes may, however, be used as nesting places; either the nest is built in a fork or else the eggs are laid in a hollow in a tree or in the abandoned nest of a crow or

A wide family

To most people ducks, geese and swans are well defined groups of birds, although the ornithologist places them all in one family. For the most part, these three types of birds are difficult to confuse with each other. There are, however, oddities that do not seem to fit conveniently into any of the three categories. The Coscoroba swan and the pigmy 'geese' are two examples of this. The division of the family into the three groups is not, however, based on proper taxonomic divisions but merely on the accepted usage of their common names. The tree ducks are an example of waterfowl being called ducks when they really belong with the swans and geese, in a group separate from the ducks. This is apparent when we examine their appearance and their behaviour closely. For example, tree ducks not only look like geese, they also behave like them. They have the same gooselike 'triumph ceremony' (see Canada goose p 356). Moreover, their courtship behaviour resembles that of swans, and includes the dipping and neck stretching typical of swans. Finally, in tree ducks, as in some swans, the male assists in the incubation.

class	**Aves**
order	**Anseriformes**
family	**Anatidae**
genus & species	*Dendrocygna arborea* black-billed
	D. arcuata wandering
	D. autumnalis red-billed
	D. bicolor fulvous
	D. javanica Indian
	D. viduata white-faced

Tree frog

Most tree frogs spend their lives in trees but a few live mainly in water, and some burrow in the ground. Nevertheless all look much alike except in their colours, although they differ widely in their breeding habits and in their calls. In Brazil and in Queensland, Australia, some tree frogs have taken to living in houses and are called house frogs.

Most tree frogs are small; the largest, the Cuban tree frog, is 5½ in. long in head and body, and 1 ft long with its legs outstretched in a jump. The smallest is 1¼ in. long in head and body. Many of them are predominantly green, but some have patches and patterns of bright colours. The most obvious feature common to all of them is that each of the toes on both fore- and hindfeet end in discs that form suckers for clinging. The toes of the forefeet are free, those of the hindfeet only partially webbed. The eyes of tree frogs are of various colours.

The 500 species are distributed over all continents except Antarctica, but are most numerous in Australasia and the Americas. They are found from sea-level to 15 000 ft.

K Boldt

Jane Burton: Photo Res.

△ In light colour phase, a European tree frog **Hyla arborea** extends its throat sac for a contemplative croak. It can reach the darker hues shown by its acrobatic congeners at left—they are on a **Juncus** rush—in a few hours.
▷ White's tree frog **Hyla caerulea,** from Australia, showing the webless front toes and climbing pads typical of all tree frogs
▽ Familiar to scientists because it does well in captivity, requiring little more than a regular diet of moths, the brilliant African tree frog **Hylambates maculatus** ranges from Mozambique to Zanzibar.

Constance P Warner

△ 'Can I unmoved see thee lying on a log, expiring frog?' . . . Charles Dickens, and White's tree frog not expiring, but in definitely relaxed mood.

Agile tree frogs

Most tree frogs are active and lively, with a few exceptions such as the species *Phyllomedusa burmeisteri* of South America which walks along branches with a hand-over-hand movement. In these species the inner toe on each foot is opposable to the others and acts as a thumb. They can cling to twigs, to the undersides of large leaves or other smooth surfaces or can creep under loose bark, clinging with their toe discs. They can leap from twig to twig, landing accurately and holding on with their discs. Some, in captivity, have shown an ability as trapeze artists, which illustrates best of all their skills among the foliage and stems of trees and bushes. The species that live mainly in water, and those that burrow, do not have such well developed discs, but they retain the leaping powers of those living in trees although they cannot cling so well. The leaping can be illustrated by the spring peeper, 1¾ in. long, which can leap 17 times its own length—about 2 ft—and the cricket frog, the same size and also from the eastern United States, which can jump 36 times its own length—about 4 ft.

Some tree frogs live in the semi-deserts in Australia. They congregate near pools and small rivers, and as these dry up in summer the frogs assemble in tightly packed masses in the mud. In this way they conserve any remaining moisture.

Musical call notes

One of the best known tree frogs lives in Brazil, and is named the smith or blacksmith frog, because its calls sound like somebody beating on metal. The cricket frog makes shrill clicking notes somewhat like the insect after which it is named, but perhaps better described as sounding like two pebbles tapped together. Indeed, a cricket frog will respond to pebbles being tapped. The golden or bell tree frog of Australia, one of the species that spends most of its time in water, sounds like a bell or a stonemason chipping with his chisel and mallet. The variety of calls can be understood from the common names of many tree frogs, such as the chorus frog, barking frog and bird-voiced frog. The spring peeper's voice sounds like the tinkle of distant sleigh bells. The canyon tree frog *Hyla arenicolor,* of California, makes a sound which to some people resembles the quack of a mallard, or the baa of a goat or a slightly hoarse lamb. In fact, it does vary a little, especially at breeding time when the male uses the different calls and the female replies.

Leaping for food

Generally, the food of tree frogs is insects, often seized in the air by the frog leaping upwards. It seems likely that tree frogs will eat any small invertebrate coming their way. Those living in water do so, their catch including, in addition to flying insects and those living in water, crayfish, spiders and centipedes. In leaping for flying insects tree frogs have taken the first step towards para-chuting. They hold their legs in such a way as to present the maximum surface to the air. The webs on the hindfeet also help so that the frog semi-parachutes to its landing place, with the insect, such as a butterfly or moth, in its mouth.

Dam-building blacksmiths

In many tree frogs the breeding follows the same lines as that of true frogs, the spawn being laid in gelatinous masses in water. Others lay their eggs singly, dropping them among water plants. The development of the tadpoles is similar to that of true frogs. Rohde's tree frog *Phyllomedusa rohdei* glues its eggs to the undersides of leaves overhanging a pond, so the tadpoles fall into the water. In some species, among them the smith frog *H. faber*, the male builds a circular dam in the shallow waters. He throws up a rampart of mud, enclosing a pool of water about 1 ft across, carefully smoothing the inner face of the rampart with his forelegs. The eggs are laid in the enclosed pool and the tadpoles develop there, protected to some extent from enemies. In one group of South American tree frogs, including Goeldi's frog *Electonotus goeldii*, the eggs are glued to the females' backs and the tadpoles later emerge from the capsules.

Boneheaded tree frogs

With rare exceptions tree frogs have no unpleasant skin secretions and are vulnerable to many enemies. Snakes, fishes and turtles eat them when they enter the water, and so do such birds as herons. There is a heavy mortality when they leave the water after turning from tadpoles into froglets. Once in the bushes and trees, where they expose themselves mainly at night, they are relatively safe. The bonyheaded frogs of Mexico to South America have an additional defence, however. They have a thick bony plate on top of their heads which is fused with the overlying skin. These frogs shelter in crevices and use the armoured top of their heads to block the opening.

Daily strip tease

Frogs shed their outer skin periodically, as do reptiles. Often they eat the cast skin, but when a frog sloughs its skin in water it is likely to leave it, and then it is eaten by any tadpoles there may be in the pond. It is often said that this shedding of the skin is associated with the growth of the frog. That is, the frog has to get rid of it to be able to expand. The explanation is not as simple as that. If it were we should be hard put to it to say why the smith frog and other tree frogs shed their skin every evening.

class	**Amphibia**
order	**Salientia**
family	**Hylidae**
genera & species	*Acris crepitans* cricket frog *Hyla aurea* golden bell tree frog *H. avivoca* bird-voiced tree frog *H. crucifer* spring peeper *H. gratiosa* barking frog *Pseudacris nigrita* chorus frog others

Tree kangaroo

As a result of adopting a tree-dwelling life, the seven species of tree kangaroos, although related to land wallabies, differ from them in appearance, particularly in the proportions of the limbs. Their fore- and hindlimbs are of almost equal length, and on the ground they take short hops with the body held nearly horizontal and the tail curving up and acting as a balancer. The head and body length is 20−30 in. and the tail is 16−37 in. long. The ears are short and rounded. The large feet have cushion-like pads underneath covered with rough skin which prevent the animal slipping when climbing, and the forefeet, much larger than the usual kangaroo's, have strong nails which help to grip branches and creepers. The well-furred tail, with a thick brush at the tip, is not prehensile but is used both as a balancer and a brace when the animal is climbing.

*The colour of the fur varies considerably in the different species. Two of the New Guinea species, **Dendrolagus goodfellowi** and **D. matschiei**, are brilliantly coloured, with reddish backs and bright yellow undersides and limbs. Of the species found in northeastern Queensland, Lumholtz's tree kangaroo is white, olive buff and black and Bennett's tree kangaroo is duller but has a dark forehead and tail-tip. The fur is usually fairly long; it is soft and silky in some species, but coarse and harsh in others. The thick fur on the nape and sometimes on the back is directed forwards and acts as a natural watershed against heavy rain when the animal is squatting in the trees with the head lower than the shoulders.*

There are five species of tree kangaroos in New Guinea and two in Queensland.

Shy and inaccessible

Tree kangaroos live in dense rain forests and although they are not rare they are seldom seen, for their native haunts are inaccessible and the animals themselves are naturally shy. Ungainly on land, they are remarkably nimble in the trees, climbing with speed and agility and jumping up to 20 ft from one tree to another. When disturbed in a tree, as when hunted by the Aborigines, they will leap to the ground from heights of 30−50 ft and there is a record of a tree kangaroo having leaped 70 ft to the ground, landing unhurt. When coming down of their own free will they descend the trees tail first. Although they sleep in the daytime in small groups in the tops of the trees, they spend much of their time on the ground, where they can move fairly rapidly. At the first sign of danger a tree kangaroo hastily seeks refuge in the trees. In Taronga Zoo, in Sydney, they entertain visitors by shinning up ropes, demonstrating how they climb through creeper-clad trees.

▷ *New Guinea tree kangaroo **Dendrolagus***

JV Clarke: Photo Res.

Graham Pizzey: Photo Res.

Leaf and fruit eater

Tree kangaroos feed mainly on the leaves of trees and creepers, on ferns and on a variety of wild fruits. They probably get nearly all the water they need in their food but tree kangaroos in captivity always drink the water supplied. In the wild they probably get enough water in the rainy season, from pockets of water in the tree forks. One of the problems of keeping them in zoos is that their natural food is difficult to obtain. Consequently they do not live long in captivity. Very little is known of their breeding habits except that there is only one young born at a time. The birth and the development in the pouch is similar to that described for the kangaroo.

Hunted with dingos

The Aborigines hunt tree kangaroos for their flesh, using the dingo or native dog to track them down. They usually hunt them very early in the morning, when the scent is freshest. One of them will climb the tree in which the animal has sought safety and try to catch it by its tail or else force it to leap to the ground where it is killed by the other hunters, known as *nulla-nullas,* who are waiting below with clubs. The kangaroo may, however, leap into another tree. Then a second hunter will climb after it.

Retracing its evolution

In the opinion of at least one distinguished Australian zoologist, Ellis Troughton, tree kangaroos, wallabies and other kangaroos all had a common tree-living ancestor. It probably had limbs of equal length and it may have had grasping feet and even a prehensile tail. Its descendants, having taken to living on the ground, took to hopping, and later leaping, perhaps because they found themselves in desert country where leaping was the best way to travel over the loose sand. So they developed long hindlegs and very short front legs. Their hindfeet also grew long, to give us the typical kangaroo. Then, following this theory, some of them took to the trees again to become the present-day tree kangaroos. Although the hindfoot is much shorter than that of a typical land-living kangaroo it is sufficiently like it to support this theory. On the principle that evolution is irreversible, the tree kangaroos have been unable to revert to their ancestral form. They have, however, gone some way to doing so. Their limbs are nearly equal in length and the front feet can grasp branches, but the hindfoot is still a non-grasping kangaroo foot and the tail is not prehensile.

class	**Mammalia**
order	**Marsupialia**
family	**Macropodidae**
genus & species	***Dendrolagus bennettianus*** *Bennett's tree kangaroo* **D. lumholtzi** *Lumholtz's tree kangaroo others*

◁ *Lumholtz's tree kangaroo among figs.*

Tree porcupine

The tree porcupines of North and South America are very different from the porcupines of the Old World. To begin with, they live mainly in trees and their hindfeet are adapted for climbing. Some species also have a prehensile tail. The best known, the Canadian or North American porcupine, is up to 3½ ft long, of which 1 ft is tail, and has an average weight of 15 lb although large males may weigh up to 40 lb. It is heavy and clumsily built with a small head, short legs and a short, stout, spiny tail. The hindfoot has a well-developed great toe and very long, powerful claws to help the animal climb. The long fur on the upper parts is brownish-black, sprinkled with long white hairs that conceal the short, barbed spines, which are yellowish-white tipped with black.

The South American tree porcupines, of which the Brazilian tree porcupine is typical, differ from the North American species in having a long, prehensile tail, the tip of which is hairless and by having only four toes on the hindfeet with a broad fleshy pad, opposable to the toes, used rather like a thumb in gripping branches when the animal is climbing. It is of lighter build with short, closely set spines, sometimes concealed by long hairs.

The Canadian porcupine inhabits most of the timbered areas of Alaska, Canada and the United States (except the southeastern quarter), south to the extreme north of Mexico. South American porcupines extend from Mexico through Central America to Colombia, Venezuela, Brazil, Bolivia, Peru and Ecuador in South America.

△ North American porcupine revealing its arsenal of over 20 000 sharp-tipped quills.
▽ Same species: long fur conceals the spines.

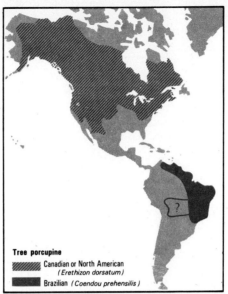

Tree porcupine
▨ Canadian or North American
   (*Erethizon dorsatum*)
■ Brazilian (*Coendou prehensilis*)

◁ *Picking a precarious path, a South American porcupine* **Coendou** *sp. seeks its typically rodent diet of bark, stems and leaves.*

No hibernation

All the tree porcupines live in wooded areas, the North American species preferring woods of conifers, junipers and poplars. Although clumsily built they can climb well and they will also swim. They lie up during the day among rocks or in hollow trees and feed mainly at dusk and at dawn. They are usually solitary but occasionally several Canadian tree porcupines may shelter together in the same den, especially in winter. They do not hibernate but they take to dens during bad weather.

Salt addicts

The Canadian tree porcupine varies its food with the seasons. In spring it eats the flowers and catkins of the willow, maple and poplar. Later it turns to the new leaves of aspen and larch. In summer it feeds more on herbaceous plants and in winter on evergreens like the hemlock and pine. Its principal food in winter, however, is bark and the porcupines do much damage by ringbarking trees. The young red firs of the Sierra Nevada in California are occasionally destroyed by tree porcupines. When the weather is bad and the snow deep an animal may live in one tree and not leave it until all the bark above the snow-line has been stripped. Tree porcupines also have a strong liking for sweet corn and a few of these animals can completely ravage a field of it.

A more peculiar taste is the porcupine's craving for salt. Handles of farm implements which have been touched by hands moistened with sweat, leaving a trace of salt, will be gnawed. So will gloves, boots, and saddles; even the steering wheel of a car has been gnawed away. The porcupine will also gnaw bones and antlers dropped by deer. But its crowning achievement is to gnaw glass bottles thrown away by campers, presumably for the salt in the glass.

The South American tree porcupines also eat the bark and leaves of trees and tender stems but in addition they eat fruit such as bananas, and occasionally corn.

James Simon: Photo Res.

Well-developed babies

The Canadian tree porcupines mate in the fall or early winter. During courtship the male rubs noses with the female and often urinates over her. Generally a single young is born after a gestation period of 210–217 days. The young are very well-developed at birth; their eyes are open and they are born with long black hair and short soft quills. They weigh about 20 oz and can climb trees when 2 days old. They are weaned in 10 days, and become sexually mature in their second year.

Little is known of the breeding habits of the South American tree porcupines. There is usually a single young at a birth, born from February to May. The young of the Brazilian tree porcupine are comparatively large at birth and are covered with long, reddish hair. Their backs are covered with short spines, which are flexible at birth.

Few natural enemies

Few animals prey on the porcupine because of its spines, but the wolverine, puma and fisher marten will attack the North American species. A tree porcupine is said never to attack an enemy. If cornered, however, it will erect its quills and turn its back on its adversary, striking out repeatedly with its tail. A porcupine does not shoot its quills but they are so lightly attached that when they enter the skin of the enemy they become detached from the porcupine.

Skulls identify species

The crested porcupine is the best known species in the Old World family Hystricidae. Not all the porcupines in that family have such prominent quills as the crested porcupine. One *Trichys lipura* living in Borneo, for example, lacks true quills. It has only short, flat, weak spines and its long tail has a brush of bristles on the end. At first sight it appears not to be a porcupine at all. The same thing can be said of some of the family Erethizontidae. Since the crested and the Canadian porcupines look so alike, the question arises: What is the essential difference between the Old World porcupines and the New World porcupines? The fact that they are widely separated geographically is not important. Both families agree in having species that show a varying tendency to grow quills among the bristly coat, and both families contain a diversity of species. Therefore, those who classify these rodents have to look for something more stable upon which to separate them. They find this in the skull. Any Old World porcupine, whatever it may have in the way of quills, has a very rounded skull which has quite obviously a different shape from that of the New World porcupines.

class	**Mammalia**
order	**Rodentia**
family	**Erethizontidae**
genera & species	***Erethizon dorsatum*** *Canadian or North American porcupine* ***Coendou prehensilis*** *Brazilian tree porcupine, others*

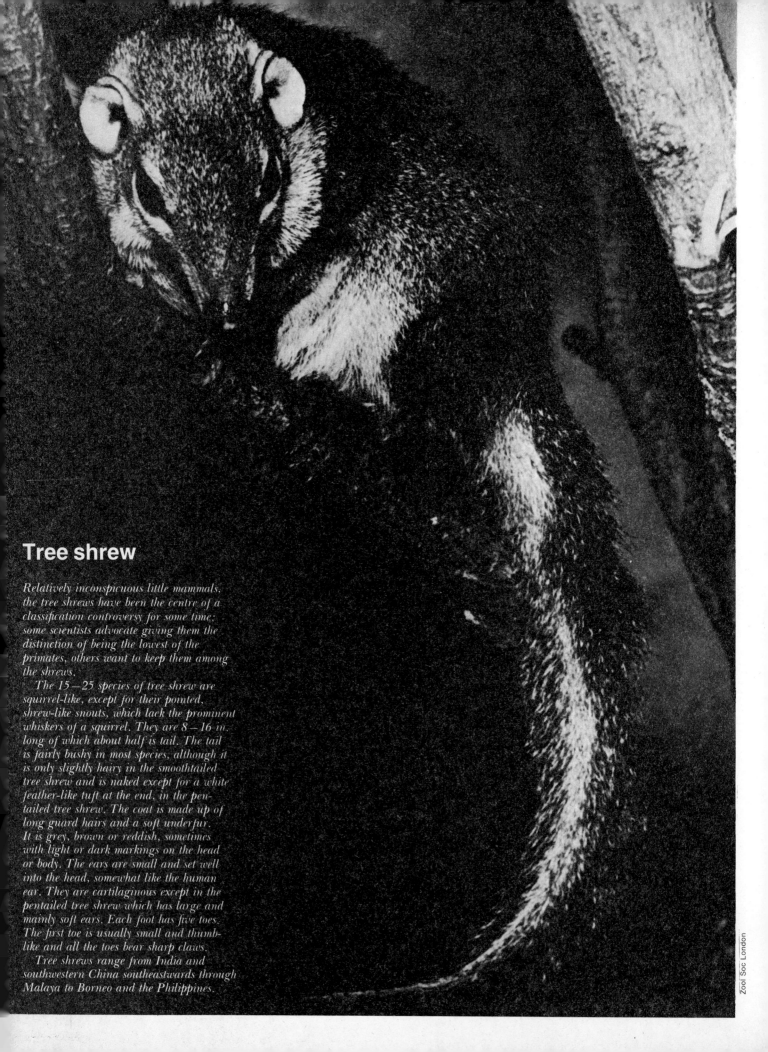

Tree shrew

*Relatively inconspicuous little mammals,
the tree shrews have been the centre of a
classification controversy for some time:
some scientists advocate giving them the
distinction of being the lowest of the
primates, others want to keep them among
the shrews.*

*The 15—25 species of tree shrew are
squirrel-like, except for their pointed,
shrew-like snouts, which lack the prominent
whiskers of a squirrel. They are 8—16 in.
long of which about half is tail. The tail
is fairly bushy in most species, although it
is only slightly hairy in the smoothtailed
tree shrew and is naked except for a white
feather-like tuft at the end, in the pentailed tree shrew. The coat is made up of
long guard hairs and a soft underfur.
It is grey, brown or reddish, sometimes
with light or dark markings on the head
or body. The ears are small and set well
into the head, somewhat like the human
ear. They are cartilaginous except in the
pentailed tree shrew which has large and
mainly soft ears. Each foot has five toes.
The first toe is usually small and thumb-
like and all the toes bear sharp claws.*

*Tree shrews range from India and
southwestern China southeastwards through
Malaya to Borneo and the Philippines.*

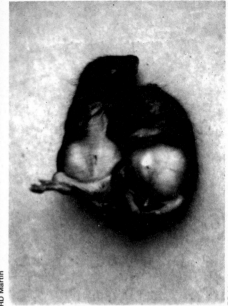

Forest dweller

Although called tree shrews—many species spend much of their time climbing in trees and bushes—they usually spend some time on the ground and some species forage there, sleeping between buttress roots of trees or under logs. All can, however, climb well. To sleep, most tree shrews roll themselves into a ball inside a nest of leaves and twigs. They run quickly on the ground or along branches, with the exception of the pentailed tree shrew, which hops or bounds. It is also the only nocturnal species. Their hearing, smell and sight are keen, and they use their voices more than shrews or squirrels, even though they are mainly solitary. Some are gregarious, living in family groups. When in danger they whimper, snort, chirp, and squeal as they bolt for cover in trees or bushes, under logs or into burrows.

Not fussy about food

Tree shrews have a very varied diet but some species take more animal food than others. The diet includes leaves, seeds and pulpy fruits, insects and worms. The Mindanao tree shrew of the Philippines has eaten mice and lizards in captivity as well as eggs. All too often in the pages of this encyclopedia general statements are made about food, much along the lines of that given here for tree shrews. It should be emphasized that these are general statements. The list of items taken by even closely related species can vary considerably and even individuals within a species may differ widely in their tastes. More important, it has not infrequently been found that when someone closely studies the diet of a particular species in the wild we find that what has been said for a long time is incorrect, or slightly so. Tree shrews have not been widely studied in the natural state, but it is fairly certain that they have a very wide range of diet.

Two-day feeds for babies

Until 1966 the information on tree shrew breeding was scanty. Then RD Martin published in *Science* (New York) an account of the birth and growth of young *Tupaia glis*.

For 1—5 days before the female gives birth the male is busy making a nest of up to 400 leaves. For the male to make a nest in which the young will be born is unique among mammals. There are usually two babies, occasionally one or three, born after a gestation of 45 days, each weighing $\frac{1}{2}$ oz. After they are born the mother spends 2 hours cleaning up the birth membranes, cutting the umbilical cord and then suckling the babies, which are born blind and naked.

By the time she leaves them the young are clean and the nest is tidy, and the stomach of each baby is swollen with milk. Each takes more than a third of its body weight at this first feed. The mother visits them again after an interval of 48 hours, and from then on she returns every two days to feed them, these being the only times she returns to the nest. The male does not enter it at all. At each visit the babies are suckled for 4—10 minutes, and the mother leaves immediately this is finished. On average each baby takes in $\frac{1}{2}$ oz of milk in 5 minutes. The babies groom themselves even at this early age, and they burrow up through the leaves to meet the mother on each visit, burrowing down again when she leaves.

Since Martin's study other tree shrews have been bred in captivity. In these, the females, not the males, built the nests. Sometimes two females shared a nest and groomed each other and one would drive off males while the other was giving birth. A group may band together against a male.

Independent infants

The young leave the nest after 4 weeks, by which time they weigh nearly 3 oz, and during that time, apart from the visits of the mother, they have to look after themselves. They make no distress calls to the mother and she makes no attempt to go to their aid when they are disturbed. She does not carry or retrieve them. The only protection they have is to make an explosive snort if disturbed and this with the violent rustling of the leaves as they move about produces a surprising effect on the human ear. Presumably it would deter a predator. The babies are sexually mature at 4 months.

△ *Tree shrews are suckled only every 2 days* *—these* **Tupaia belangeri** *have just been fed and lie bloated after their mammoth milk meal.* ◁△ *Hygienic preliminaries: grooming activity is more frequent in pregnant tree shrews such as this* **T. belangeri** *from Thailand.* ◁ *A pensive tree shrew* **T. glis**.

Anatomical puzzle

The relationships of tree shrews have long been in doubt. At first they were classified with true shrews (p 2129), then placed in a separate order, the Menotyphla, with the elephant shrews (p 717). They have also been placed in the order Primates because they were thought to be related to lemurs (p 1303). They have even been spoken of as possibly representing the very early type of animal from which monkeys, apes and man are descended. They have a well-developed brain and other features of their anatomy are also similar to those of the higher primates, including an eye-socket completely encircled by bone which occurs in all species except the pentailed tree shrew. Martin takes the view that they are related to marsupials on the one hand and rabbits (p 1886) on the other, but only because, like these, tree shrews are primitive mammals. Certainly their early life history is very like that of the rabbit. Martin therefore suggests they should be placed in a separate order, the Tupaioidea. There is much to be said for this when there is so much doubt.

class	**Mammalia**
order	**Tupaioidea**
family	**Tupaiidae**
genera & species	***Dendrogale murina*** *smoothtailed tree shrew* ***Ptilocercus lowi*** *pentailed tree shrew* ***Tupaia glis*** *tree shrew* ***Urogale everetti*** *Mindanao tree shrew others*

Tree snake

Many snakes live in trees. Some, like the boomslang (p 269) and some of the rear-fanged snakes (p 1922), have already been dealt with. Attention is given here to the tree snakes of southern and southeast Asia which are not only the most adept at climbing among trees but have also earned the name of 'flying snakes'.

One of the best known is the paradise tree snake of Malaya. It is black but there is a bright green spot on each of its scales, so it seems to have a regular pattern of green spots. It also has a row of four-petalled red spots along its back. Its underside is yellowish green. The golden tree snake ranges from Ceylon through southeast Asia to the Philippines. It is black with golden yellow to orange markings and red spots on its back. Tree snakes are up to 5 ft long and are very slender, with a tail that is nearly half the length of the head and body.

Umbrella ribs

Tree snakes are most accomplished climbers, able to go up almost vertical walls or tree trunks by making use of every little irregularity in the surface. They are helped in this by a well marked angularity along each side of the body and tail. They can also spring across gaps of 3–4 ft, in an almost vertical position. This remarkable feat is performed by the snake coiling itself loosely over a branch then straightening explosively. The most famous exploit of tree snakes is, however, to drop through the air in a glide, either from bough to bough or from tree to ground. The snake holds its body rigid and launches itself into the air, and at the same time it 'draws in its belly'. Part of this action involves spreading the outer ends of the ribs. On each side of the ventral scales is a suture and by muscular contraction the outer ends of each scale are drawn down and slightly in, so the whole lower surface becomes concave, trapping a cushion of air beneath it. The effect is similar to that of dropping a stick of bamboo split lengthwise. The split bamboo falls more slowly than a comparable piece of bamboo stem that is intact, and it descends more nearly in the

horizontal position. The tree snakes are even said to help the forward movement of the glide by alternately inflating and drawing in their belly.

Hunting by sight

When actively hunting a tree snake glides slowly and almost noiselessly to the top of a tree then slides slowly down to the lower branches, looking for lizards, geckos and similar prey. In such hunting sight is the best way of locating a target. Related snakes, belonging to the same subfamily, are known to use binocular vision. They have a long horizontal pupil and the sides of the snout are hollowed out in front of the eyes, forming grooves. Light from objects directly in front of the snout travels along the groove, enters the front of each eye and strikes the retina on the other side of the eye. This almost certainly gives binocular and stereoscopic vision, demonstrated by the way such snakes turn their heads to follow the movements of anything they are investigating.

Long-term family planning

A related North American snake *Leptodeira annulata,* known as the cat-eyed snake, is remarkable for the behaviour of one member of its species which laid a clutch of fertile eggs after having been kept on its own for 6 years. There are other examples of a female snake in captivity producing several clutches of fertile eggs at intervals of about a month. Presumably, therefore, some female snakes can store sperm inside their bodies for use over long periods. Whether this is general for tree snakes is not known. In fact, in spite of their being numerous and widespread, and known for a long time, we are very ignorant of their breeding habits except to say that they lay eggs.

Ignorance dispelled

This is not the only aspect of their way of life that has suffered from lack of knowledge. The 'flying' habit is another. As is usual when information is lacking legend and folklore take the upper hand. In Malaya and Indonesia it was believed that to get from tree to tree the snake changed into a bird and flew. Moreover, it remained in this guise until a real bird alighted nearby, when it immediately changed back to a snake and seized the bird. Zoologists were not taken in by such stories, nor were they prepared to believe the snake could fly, or even glide, until Major Stanley Flower kept some tree snakes in captivity. It is not easy to induce a tree snake to throw itself through the air, but Major Flower finally induced his pets to leap from the top windows of his house to the lower branches of a tree several yards away.

Looping along: a green tree snake **Philothamnus irregularis** *winds its way through an African tree.*

Jane Burton: Photo Res.

class	**Reptilia**
order	**Squamata**
suborder	**Serpentes**
family	**Colubridae**
genus & species	***Chrysopelea ornata*** *golden tree snake* ***C. paradisi*** *paradise tree snake others*

Tree squirrel

*Plenty of squirrels live in trees to a greater or lesser extent. Tree squirrels are the 55 species belonging to the genus **Sciurus** that are distributed over Europe, most of Asia and America from southern Canada to the eastern United States. Two of the best known and most widespread are the grey squirrel of North America and the red squirrel of Europe and Asia, and attention will be given to these.*

Tree squirrels differ from ground squirrels (p 966) and flying squirrels (p 804) in having bushy tails about as long as head and body combined. They range from 16 to 26 in. in total length and weigh up to 3 lb. Their coat is grey to red, sometimes black, with white or cream, sometimes yellow or orange, underparts. The winter coat is usually slightly different to the summer coat and although the body fur is moulted twice a year the tail is moulted only once. The tail is always well furred and in many species it is flattened — feathery rather than bushy. The ears usually have tufts of hair at the tips but these are retained for only part of the year in some species. The four toes on the front feet and the five toes on the hind feet bear sharp claws.

Arboreal acrobats

Tree squirrels forage on the ground but quickly escape to trees when disturbed. They shin rapidly up a trunk, their first leap taking them 3–4 ft up after which their sharp claws are used in a bounding climb. They can run along a branch or hang from it, travelling upside down by using all four feet hand over hand. The grey squirrel, especially, is a skilled acrobat. It will hang by its hindfeet from one branch to reach food on a branch below. It will leap gracefully from the outer branches of one tree to those of another over a distance of 12 ft. As it sails through the air the legs are spreadeagled and the flattened tail acts both as a balancer and a rudder.

A tree squirrel's usual reaction to an intruder is to scold, then to disappear behind a trunk or stout branch, all the time keeping the trunk or branch between itself and its enemy. When forced to do so it will drop to the ground for escape, from heights of 30 ft or more, plunging into undergrowth like an arrow or dropping straight down on all fours onto bare earth or short turf.

Scattered stores

Although primarily vegetarian, eating nuts, berries, soft fruits, buds and some fungi, most tree squirrels take birds' eggs and nestlings, even carrion. They are traditionally hoarders but so far as the grey and the European red squirrels are concerned they seldom cache food in the way traditionally attributed to them. Stores of nuts buried in the ground or in a hollow tree are more likely to be the work of fieldmice. A squirrel buries nuts, acorns or berries singly and well spaced out. It carries the food in its mouth, stops at a chosen spot, digs a hole

with a quick action of the forefeet, just deep enough to take the nut or acorn, then pushes the earth back with the forefeet.

Importance of chewing

It has been shown that a young grey squirrel does not open a nut efficiently the first time but learns to gnaw it open. Although all adult grey squirrels open nuts in the same way, showing that the pattern of this behaviour is species specific — all members of the species do it the same way, 'by instinct' — the instinct has to be reinforced by learning.

The front teeth of squirrels gr[ow continu]ously at the roots and it is usuall[y said that] their habit of chewing objects o[ther than] food is necessary to keep the te[eth worn] down to normal length. Possibly son[e of the] damage done to trees comes fr[om this] chewing habit, but the way grey squirrels chew the lead labels on ornamental trees in parks and gardens is perhaps the best illustration of the habit. Recently, however, it has been shown that squirrels, and rats also, are constantly grinding their teeth, when not otherwise engaged, and it is this that keeps them the required length.

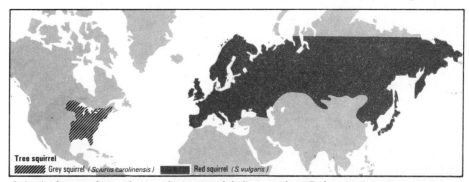

Tree squirrel
////// Grey squirrel (*Sciurus carolinensis*)   ▮ Red squirrel (*S. vulgaris*)

△ *Squirrel ranges before the spread of grey and decline of red.* ▽ *Red squirrel gnawing a titbit.*

Nest of twigs and leaves

Tree squirrels build nests, or dreys, in the branches of trees and these are used for several purposes, one being for a nursery. Each squirrel usually builds several in adjacent trees. They are bulky structures composed of twigs, strips of thin bark, leaves and moss. Some are cup-shaped, others domed. Sometimes an old bird's nest, such as one made by a crow, is used as a foundation. The breeding or nursery nest is often a huge ball of leaves and sticks in a roomy hollow in a tree trunk. The breeding season of the European red squirrel varies with latitude. In the northern parts of the range the only breeding period is spring. In the southern parts there are two periods, January—April and May—August. Gestation is 46 days, the litters consisting of 1—6 young, usually 3 or 4, born blind and naked. They are weaned at 7—10 weeks. In the grey squirrel mating takes place between early January and August. There are usually two litters a year. Gestation is 44 days, and other details of development are much the same as in the red squirrel.

John Markham

Jane Burton: Photo Res.

△ Already confident, a young grey squirrel climbs among the branches of a horse-chestnut, dangling its tail. This acts as both balance and rudder as the squirrel bounds among foliage.
◁ Nursery in the tree tops—the grey squirrel builds several dreys in adjoining trees, one of which acts as a nursery. The nest is built from twigs, bark, leaves and moss and is easily visible among the bare branches in winter.

Declining enemies

Tree squirrels are remarkably skilful not only in moving among trees but in keeping out of sight once they are alerted to possible danger. This is well illustrated by the occasion when a professional pest exterminator was brought in to clear a garden of a dozen squirrels—the estimated number made by the people living there. In a few days he shot more than three times that number. In much of Europe the natural enemies of squirrels have been largely eliminated. What these could be, throughout the range of tree squirrels, can be judged from the natural enemies of grey squirrels in North America. They include the goshawk and red-shouldered hawk, barred owl and horned owl, and tree-climbing snakes, and, on the ground the fox and the bobcat; finally, and probably most important, the pine marten, which can move through trees at least as skilfully as the nimble squirrel.

Rapid tooth growth

At one time the only way to demonstrate the remarkable speed of growth of the incisors of rodents was to show what happened if two of the incisors were awry and failed to bite on each other. They curved into the mouth eventually locking the jaws so that the animal died of starvation. In the last 30—40 years accurate measurements have been made of their rate of growth. Although the figures are not known for tree squirrels we can be reasonably sure they compare fairly closely with those that are known. The incisors of the common rat grow up to 6 in. in a year, those of the guinea pig up to 10 in. and those of the pocket gopher up to 14 in. in a year. The pocket gopher uses its teeth for digging and needs a rapid growth rate to counteract a high rate of wear. So it would seem that the rate of growth is related to the uses to which the teeth are put.

class	**Mammalia**
order	**Rodentia**
family	**Sciuridae**
genus & species	*Sciurus carolinensis* grey squirrel *S. vulgaris* red squirrel others

Triggerfish

Triggerfishes have a spine on the back with an ingenious locking device, so that it remains erect until the spine behind it is depressed to release it. This is, however, only one of their many peculiarities.

The triggerfish's body is deep and compressed, and seen from the side it is almost diamond-shaped. The head occupies about a third of the length, the mouth is small, and the eyes fairly large. Just behind the eye is a short dorsal fin with spines, the first two making the locking device. The second dorsal fin is long and high; the anal fin is the same shape and lies exactly opposite it. The pectoral fins are small and the pelvic fins are no more than short spines. The body, seldom more than 2 ft long, is covered with small rhomboidal bony plates, their outer surfaces bearing one or more small spines. As if artificially coloured, triggerfishes are often boldly marked with garish, sometimes almost grotesque patterns.

The filefishes, formerly placed in a separate family, are near relatives. They are similar in shape but usually up to only 1 ft long, and there is a single spine on the back, level with or in front of the eye. Although single it can still be locked in place. Its scales also carry more spines, so its surface looks velvety, yet is rough to touch—like a file. Moreover, the second dorsal and the anal fins are not so high. In place of pelvic fins there is a spine on the pelvic bone, which can move freely and is connected to the body by a wide flap of skin.

Both triggerfishes and filefishes live mainly in tropical coastal waters.

Dignified movement

The way in which triggerfishes and filefishes swim, is especially interesting. Although the two look alike and are now placed in the same family, an indication of how closely related they are, their swimming techniques are quite different. Both swim slowly with the body rigid, in what looks like a dignified manner. The triggerfishes swim by a simultaneous flapping of the dorsal and anal fins. In contrast, filefishes are driven through the water by waves passing backwards along these fins.

There is a second contrast, connected with their defence. The locking spine seems to be used when the triggerfish takes refuge in a crevice in rock or coral. It erects the spine and cannot be pulled out. It is impossible to press the spine down with the finger but the fish can lower it by dropping the second spine, which releases the large spine in front of it. The fish can be made to lower the first spine if the third one is pressed down. When a triggerfish is looked at from any but the side view its compressed body presents only a fairly thin edge. This is probably useful to a triggerfish for concealment, simply because as it turns it is transformed from an obvious large, solid rhomboidal object to something as incon-

△ Abstract art: the strident, garish daubings on a Pacific triggerfish **Rhinecanthus aculeatus** — one of the two species called humahuma-nukanuka-a-puaa — have earned it the name of Picasso fish.

△ A spotted triggerfish **Balistoides conspicillum** near coral, into which it dives when frightened.
▽ Ladylike warpaint: the queen triggerfish **Balistes vetula** lives in the Atlantic and Indian Oceans.

spicuous as a knife blade seen edge on. According to William Beebe, the celebrated American marine zoologist, at least one species of filefish *Alutera scriptus* goes one better. It stands on its head among clumps of eelgrass with its fins gently waving, and with its mottled green colour the fish is hard to tell from the eelgrass.

Shell-crackers

Both triggerfish and filefish have teeth implanted in sockets in the jaws, which is unusual for any fish. The triggerfishes have eight chisel-like teeth in each jaw which they use to hack holes in the shells of mussels, oysters and clams to eat the soft flesh inside, or to crack crabs and other crustaceans. They also eat carrion. Filefish are, as far as we know, vegetarian.

Spiny deterrent?

Little worth mentioning is known about the breeding habits or the enemies of triggerfishes. It is assumed that the spines might stick in the throat or damage the mouth of a predator. It could be argued that their striking colours are warning colours, so any predator taking a bite and suffering injury would leave the next triggerfish or filefish alone. It has also been suggested that the fishes may be poisonous, but so far the only evidence is that triggerfishes may sometimes be poisonous to eat when they themselves have eaten contaminated shellfish or carrion; any poison is of the *ciguatera* kind (p 1860). There is still the curious pelvic spine to account for, especially in the filefishes, with its flap of skin. It has been suggested that this spine is used by the fish for fixing itself in crevices in rocks or coral, as a defensive measure, just as the triggerfish uses its spines.

People who have handled these fishes report that they can inflict deep bites with their strong sharp teeth. Triggerfishes and filefishes may not be as defenceless as their slow moving habits suggest. This seems to be supported by the fact that they make sounds — usually a sign of strong territorial instinct or an ability to defend themselves or both. Some triggerfishes grate their teeth together in the roof and floor of the throat. Other types, as well as the filefishes, rub together the bases of their fin spines. In all the fish, the sounds are amplified by resonance in the swimbladder. At least one species, the black durgon, of the West Indies, makes a rapid puttering sound by vibrating a membrane in front of its pectoral fins.

Why so colourful?

One species of triggerfish living in the tropical eastern Atlantic and the Mediterranean often wanders as far north as the British Isles in summer. It is grey-brown to green-brown with a violet tinge on the back and blue bands and yellow or black spots on the dorsal and anal fins. This is a sober colouring compared with most. The undulate triggerfish of the Indo-Pacific is purplish with small orange spots on the face, orange lines all over the body and golden orange fins. The humahuma-nuka-nuka-a-puaa of the southern Pacific has such a bizarre pattern it has been named the Picasso fish. Others are equally remarkable for their extraordinary colours and patterns. According to Craig Phillips, in *The Captive Sea*, triggerfishes are light-shy. He describes how those he had in an aquarium panicked when the light was suddenly switched on, and they put on an unusual facial expression, as if they were about to spit. All this suggests that triggerfishes must hide their splendid colours, which makes it even more puzzling why they should have them.

Heinz Eder

class	**Pisces**
order	**Tetraodontiformes**
family	**Balistidae**
genera & species	***Balistes capriscus*** *eastern Atlantic* ***Melichthys radula*** *black durgon* ***Rhinecanthus aculeatus*** *Picasso fish* *others*

◁ *Submarine seascape Nibbling from a honeycomb-like coral is an undulate triggerfish* **Balistapus undulatus.** *Solitary, slow and ponderous, the triggerfish is a tropical marine species. Adding to this underwater scene are two very spiny sea urchins tucked away in crevices in the mound of dead coral.*

Trogon

The trogons are beautifully coloured, fairly large, tropical birds, the most brilliant of which, the quetzal or resplendent trogon, is described on page 1884. Although ranging throughout the tropics the 35 or more species of trogon are remarkably alike in body form. They range in size from 9 to 13 in., and have rounded wings and short blunt bills. The tail is long and although the tail feathers are of unequal length, it is kept folded, so it appears to be square. The feet are very small, with two toes facing forwards and two backwards. Trogons have the second, or inner, toe facing backwards instead of the fourth, or outer, toe as in woodpeckers, parrots and some other birds. Extremely delicate skin is another trogon peculiarity; the preparation of specimens is a taxidermist's nightmare. Even when the skin is prepared, the soft feathers fall out if it is handled and, moreover, the colours fade. The male's plumage is the brighter. The upperparts are usually green, blue or brown, and the underparts bright red, orange or yellow.

△ *Propped woodpecker-like on its tail feathers, a male scarlet-rumped trogon* **Harpactes duvauceli** *hunts for insects. It lives in Malaya, Sumatra and Borneo, and, like most male trogons, is more gaily coloured than the female.*

Trogons range from America, where most are found, through Africa south of the Sahara, India, southern China, the East Indies and the Philippines. Very few are found outside the tropics. The elegant trogon breeds as far north as northern Arizona and the Narina trogon ranges from Liberia to the Cape Province.

Constance P Warner

*South American pavonine quetzal **Pharomachrus pavoninus**, showing unusual toe arrangement.*

fruit and their notched bills probably assist in the rapid plucking necessary for the successful execution of this aerobatic trick.

Stealing by eating

Very little is known of the social life of trogons, but for most of the year they are solitary. During the breeding season the males of some species gather in small groups. Most American trogons appear to have a poor courtship song; it is little more than an elaborate form of the simple call.

The nest is always in a cavity, such as the abandoned hole of a woodpecker or a natural hole in a rotten stump. Very often a special hole is excavated, but as trogons' bills are short and weak they can dig in only very rotten wood. Some, however, make their homes in the nests of termites or wasps. The gartered trogon uses the papery wasps' nests that are suspended from the branches of trees. Before starting to dig the bird eats the wasps and as it tears out the combs it eats the larvae. The nest of the blue-throated trogon is no more than a pear-shaped cavity, 3—4 in. across and twice as high, in which the trogon sits with its long tail turned up over its back. The nest is not lined and the 2—4 white eggs are incubated for about 18 days. Both members of the pair share the work of digging the hole, incubating and feeding the chicks. In the blue-throated trogon the male incubates by day and the female from late afternoon to the following morning.

Deranged father

Alexander Skutch has described how a male Mexican trogon was slow in feeding its chicks. For the first couple of days after they had hatched the male brought insects to the nest but did not give them to the chicks. Instead he ignored their clamouring and flew away. This contrasts with the zeal of the male song tanagers (p 2356) who tried to feed their eggs. A bird must start feeding its offspring instinctively because there can be no previous training or example. The instinct is presumably released by the sight of the chicks in the nest. In some patterns of instinctive behaviour there is more than a simple switching-on in response to a stimulus; the actions have to be perfected by learning. In the case of the Mexican trogon the feeding behaviour was 'switched on' but there must have been some kind of temporary fault that took a couple of days to clear, after which the trogon was able to finish the sequence of actions by dropping its load into a waiting mouth. This comparison with a machine may seem inappropriate, yet the fact remains that the emergence of instinctive patterns is largely automatic and, as with the best-made machines, the works can sometimes go wrong.

Born layabouts

Trogons are mainly forest birds, but are also found in plantations where there are sufficient trees. As with so many brightly-coloured birds of the tropical forests they are quite inconspicuous, as the bold patches of colour break up the outlines of their bodies in the light and shadow of the upper layers of the forest. Trogons are often described as lethargic; they will perch motionless with their bodies upright, for minutes at a time. Their simple calls, consisting of various coos, hoots and whistles, are sometimes ventriloquial, so increasing the difficulty of locating the trogons.

Plucking insects and fruit

Trogons are most easily spotted when they are feeding because they forage like fly-catchers. Flying insects are only occasionally caught, however, and the most frequent prey of trogons is insects which they pluck from leaves and twigs while hovering. The broad bill is surrounded by bristles which form a net for trapping insects. Other small animals such as snails, small tree frogs and lizards are also plucked from the foliage. Many trogons also eat fruit by the same method, plucking it from the stem in flight then carrying it back to the perch. The American trogons are particularly fond of

class	**Aves**		
order	**Trogoniformes**		
family	**Trogonidae**		
genera & species	***Apaloderma narina*** *Narina trogon*		
	Trogon elegans *elegant trogon*		
	T. mexicanus *Mexican trogon*		
	T. rufus *blue-throated trogon*		
	T. violaceus *gartered trogon*		
	others		

Tropicbird

The tropicbirds are seabirds with an easy wheeling flight, their graceful appearance enhanced by their long tail plumes. They are related to cormorants, pelicans and boobies, but in appearance and habits they resemble the terns in some respects and the petrels in others. They range from 32 to 40 in. long but about half this length is made up of two very long, streaming tail feathers. Without these, they are only 16 – 24 in. long. The bill is thick and slightly curved, the legs are short and the feet are webbed. The plumage is white, sometimes tinged with pink, with black eye-stripes and black on the wings.

There are three species of tropicbird, all living in the tropics. Captain John Smith, writing in 1622, said of this bird that its name derived from the places where it was most seen. The red-billed tropicbird is found in the Atlantic, Pacific and Indian Oceans, including the Red and Caribbean Seas. The upperparts of this species are barred with black. The yellow-billed tropicbird also lives in these three oceans and is common in the Caribbean Sea and can be distinguished by the solid black marking on the wings. The largest, the red-tailed tropicbird, is almost pure white or pink except for the black eye-stripes and the red tail streamers. It is found in the Pacific and the southern Indian Ocean.

▽ X-ray: a red-tailed tropicbird with every detail of its wing feathers outlined by glare.

At home in the air

Tropicbirds have a fast, rather pigeon-like flight, and they spend more time in the air than any of their relatives except perhaps the frigatebirds (p 816). Outside the breeding season they may be found in ones and twos well out to sea. They do not settle on the sea very often, and when they do they are poor swimmers. They come to land only during the breeding season. Their legs are so short and set so far back that tropicbirds can only shuffle awkwardly and can hardly lift their bodies off the ground. Their nesting places are usually on cliffs, from which they can launch themselves into the air with the minimum of effort.

Plummet to feed

In their feeding habits, tropicbirds closely resemble terns. They fly at a height of about 50 ft with head turned down and bill held vertical, like terns. When food is spotted a tropicbird hovers on rapidly beating wings then plunges into the sea with hardly a splash. A moment later it surfaces, shakes itself with wings and tail raised and springs into the air. The food is fish and squid, taken by grasping with the sharp edges of the bill.

Behave like petrels

On the Galapagos, Ascension Island and some other places, tropicbirds nest all the year round, probably because there is an even supply of food throughout the year. Nesting takes place on islands, starting with a long courtship period in which small groups of tropicbirds chase each other through the sky. Courtship also takes place on the nests, which are no more than bare patches of ground in crevices or under rocks. There is competition for suitable sites and fighting often breaks out, the birds sparring with their bills and sometimes injuring each other.

A single brown and white egg is incubated by both parents for periods of several days at a time. The chick emerges in about six weeks and another two months or more elapse before it leaves the nest. It hatches with a covering of down and develops slowly, being left alone after a while, as both parents go away to feed. During this stage many tropicbird chicks are killed in the squabbles for nest sites. The chick leaves the nest when two months old. By this time the parents have deserted it and it will have lost weight. This desertion, the long nestling period and the shuffling gait on land are all reminiscent of the behaviour of the petrels.

Cropping their tails

As tropicbirds nest on islands, sometimes well out to sea, they suffer from few enemies, the main cause of death apparently being the attacks by adults on nestlings. Like many other seabirds that nest in isolated places tropicbirds are fearless and will even allow themselves to be lifted off the nest. In the West Indies this tameness has led to their being killed by rats and in Bermuda their eggs were once collected for food. Otherwise tropicbirds have suffered little from man. On some Pacific Islands they suffered considerable indignity when the local peoples pulled the long tail feathers from nesting birds for use as ornaments. Perhaps the main danger today comes, however, from cats or rats introduced to islands. While a parent is on the nest it not only sits tight but will try to defend itself; this lays it open to a quick death from a cat or a full grown rat. Also, when the parents leave the nests the chicks are even more vulnerable to these two predators.

Boatswain birds

Tropicbirds are a familiar sight to sailors in tropical regions. They do not follow ships, like albatrosses or storm petrels, but investigate ships that cross their path. In French, tropicbirds are known as *paille-en-queue* and an English sailors' name for them is 'marlinspike', which alludes to the outline of their broad bodies and their long, narrow tail feathers. A more common alternative is 'bo'sun bird' or 'boatswain bird', which some people say is from the resemblance of their twittering calls to the boatswain's pipe, while others claim it is from their rolling gait when on land. Scientifically they are named after Phaëthon, the son of Apollo, who dived headlong from the sky and fell into the sea.

John Warham

KB Newman

class	**Aves**
order	**Pelecaniformes**
family	**Phaethontidae**
genus & species	*Phaethon aethereus* red-billed tropicbird **P. lepturus** yellow-billed tropicbird **P. rubricauda** red-tailed tropicbird

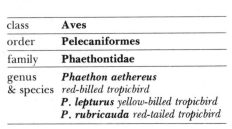

◁ △ *Staying put come what may, a nearly fledged red-tailed tropicbird crouches on the ground beside its watchful parent.*
◁ *A sheltered hollow makes a secure nest site for this yellow-billed tropicbird but accommodating the tail feathers is a problem.*

Trout

The European trout, of very variable colour, is known by three names. The brown trout is small, dark and non-migratory. It can weigh up to 17 lb 12 oz and lives in the smaller rivers and pools. The lake trout is larger and paler. It lives in larger rivers and lakes and it may be migratory. The sea trout, large, silvery up to 4½ ft long and weighing up to 30 lb, is distinctly migratory. All three belong to the same species.

The European brown trout and brook trout are greenish brown, the flanks being lighter than the back, and the belly yellowish. They are covered with many red and black spots, the latter surrounded by pale rings. There are spots even on the gill covers. These two and the sea trout resemble the salmon in shape and appearance except that the angle of the jaw reaches to well behind the eye and the adipose fin is tinged with orange.

The North American species are similar. The cut-throat trout has two red marks across the throat. The Dolly Varden is named for its conspicuous red spots, coloured like the cherry ribbons worn by the Dickens character. In the brook trout the pattern is more mottled but it also has red spots on the flanks. The rainbow trout has a reddish band along the flanks. The lake or mackinau trout lives in deep water, down to 400 ft. The golden trout lives in water 8 000 ft or more above sea level.

△ As trout grow, they take a larger proportion of other fish; the victim here is a small chub.
◁ Small fry: most of these young trout will fall victim to predators, including larger trout.

2413

◁ *Like some figment of an angler's daydream, a big New Zealand rainbow trout jumps from its shoal for a flying titbit.*

▷ *The American brook trout, a fish of fast water and clear lakes. Unlike other trout, it does not move from its home waters to spawn.*

▽ *Mixed bunch, with rainbow trout in front of brown. Because of aquarium glass, the red line on the rainbows' sides cannot be seen.*

Clean-living fish

Trout grow best in clear, aerated waters and although they are sometimes found in turbid waters it is only when the surface layers are well supplied with oxygen. They are readily affected by silt; it may spoil their spawning sites, reduce their food supply or act directly on the fishes themselves. Laboratory experiments have shown that particles in suspension in the water, at a level as low as 270 parts per million, abrade the gills or cause them to thicken. The rate of growth of trout varies in other ways as well, often to a remarkable extent, with the conditions of their surroundings. Temperature, for instance, is highly important, and an example can be seen at the time when they resume feeding after the winter fast. Normally, trout stop feeding in autumn and resume in spring, in about March when the water reaches a temperature of 2°C/36°F or more. In a mild winter they may begin feeding in December and continue until the first cold snap of the following autumn.

The rate of growth also varies from one river to another, or from river to sea. Trout living in small streams grow more slowly than those in large rivers, and those in large bodies of fresh water grow more slowly than those living in the sea. A trout in a small river will grow 2½, 5 and 8 in. in its first, second and third years respectively. Corresponding figures for a sea trout will be 3—5, 4—5 and 10—11 in.

A maturing diet

The diet of trout varies with their age. Fry eat mainly aquatic larvae of insects, rarely the adults. Later they eat large numbers of winged insects, as well as water fleas and freshwater shrimps. When adult they eat mainly small fishes as well as shrimps, insect larvae and adults, especially the winged insects. Sea trout feed on sprats, young herring and sand eels and also on a large percentage of small crustaceans, including shrimps and prawns.

Correct place to spawn

Male trout begin to breed at two years, females at three, returning to do so to the place where they themselves were hatched. This homing has been verified experimentally, by transporting marked trout to other parts of a river system, then finding them later, back on their 'home ground'. Breeding usually takes place from October to February, the time varying from one locality to another. Spawning is normally in running water, trout living in lakes going into the feeder streams.

For spawning the female makes a 'redd' in gravelly shallows, digging a depression with flicks of her tail. As she lays her eggs, the male, in attendance on her, fertilises them, stationing himself beside her but slightly to the rear. It has been found that a successful redd is one with a current flowing downwards through the gravel. The eggs hatch in about 40 days. The fry are ½—1 in. long at hatching, and the yolk sac is absorbed in 4—6 weeks.

Surrounded by enemies

WE Frost and ME Brown, in their book *The Trout*, state that 94% of fry are lost during the first 3—4 months of their lives. After this the mortality drops to 20%. Eels are often said to kill trout and especially to ravage the spawning grounds, but there is no evidence of this. The chief enemies of trout are water shrew, mink, the common rat, and to some extent otters and herons. Another enemy of trout is larger trout. Well grown ones have sometimes been found to have another trout, 5—6 in. long, in their stomachs. The record for the brown trout comes from New Zealand, where the fish were introduced. In 1967 a 20lb trout had a foot-long trout in its stomach. In their cannibalism, therefore, trout vie with pike, always regarded as a traditional enemy, which, with few exceptions, take only medium to large sized trout.

There are two other contributors to trout depletion—apart from man. Numbers of other animals compete with it for food, and of these, which include several water birds, the eel is probably one of the worst, more so in rivers than in lakes. The other natural 'enemy' is lack of oxygen, especially during the winter. When the pools and lakes are frozen over, trout must rely on oxygen trapped under ice. This is replenished by oxygen given out by water plants. When, however, the ice is blanketed by snow, light does not penetrate, plants cannot 'work', and trout are asphyxiated.

Slaughter of species

The wide variation in size and colour of the European trout is brought out by the history of its species. In 1758 Linnaeus named three species: the Swedish river trout, the sea trout and the brook trout. Dr Albert Günther, leading authority on fishes, wrote in 1880: 'We know of no other group of fishes which offers so many difficulties . . . to the distinction of species'. He recognized 10 species in the British Isles alone—the sea trout, sewin, phinnock, Galway sea trout, Orkney sea trout, river trout, great lake trout, gillaroo, Welsh blackfinned trout and Loch Leven trout. Thirty years later, C Tate Regan, Günther's successor, put forward strong arguments for treating these and all species and races in continental Europe as one very variable species.

class	**Pisces**
order	**Salmoniformes**
family	**Salmonidae**
genera & species	***Salmo aguabonita*** *golden* ***S. clarki*** *cutthroat* ***S. gairdneri*** *rainbow* ***S. trutta*** *brown* ***Salvelinus fontinalis*** *brook* ***S. malma*** *Dolly Varden* ***S. namaycush*** *lake, others*

Adult brown trout, easily identified by the red spots on the side of its body, swims in clear river water; the clearer the water, the faster it grows.

WT Davidson

Bluntnosed troutperch—at only 6 in. long, a diminutive offshoot of an ancient perch stock, and easy prey for both namesakes.

Malcolm McGregor

Troutperch

When a fish looks like a trout yet in some ways resembles a perch, the obvious name to give it is troutperch. We now know, however, that it is related to neither. The only two species live in North America. The first, the bluntnosed troutperch or sandroller, is found in the freshwaters of most of Canada, from Quebec to Alaska and southwards to Virginia, Kentucky, Missouri and Kansas. The second, merely called a troutperch, is more localised, being found in the basin of the Columbia river, in western North America. Both are small, the first up to 6 in. long, the second up to 4 in. The body has much the same shape as a trout, yet it also recalls the appearance of a perch. There are the same number of fins as in a trout but they are spiny as in a perch, with one or more stout spines in the leading margin of the dorsal, anal and pelvic fins. There is, however, an adipose fin, as in trout. The body is covered with spiny scales and is spotted. The head is rather pointed, the mouth is small, the eye large, and when freshly caught troutperch have a peculiar translucent appearance.

Fish of humble station

Troutperch are common in the larger streams and in deep clear lakes, especially those with sandy or gravel bottoms. These small shoaling fishes lead uneventful lives, feeding on aquatic insects and small freshwater crustaceans. They are important only as food for the various kinds of predatory fishes, such as trout and pike, or as livebait for fishermen. Lacking attractive colours or any special features of behaviour troutperch have not been closely studied. They have not even caught the fancy of aquarists. The only aspect of these two species that has caused any particular stir in zoological

circles is that they used to be regarded as a kind of missing link between the salmon family and the perch family. More recent studies have shown, however, that troutperch are an evolutionary offshoot of the perches that were probably once much more widespread, with many more species.

Running water spawners

In late May or early June in the southern parts of the range, slightly later in the north, troutperches move to sandbars in the lakes. They spawn in water not more than 3½ ft deep and in lakes with no suitable shallow waters the shoals ascend the feeder streams. In the rivers they go upstream. There is much jostling among the members of the shoal as they sort themselves out, more or less into pairs, but more often with one female attended by two or more males. Fertilisation is external, and the eggs, $\frac{1}{18}$ in. diameter, sticky and heavier than water, sink to the bottom to adhere to the coarser gravel or rocks in the rapid waters of the streams.

Unsung but essential

Throughout the animal world there are some species, and troutperch seem to be one of them, whose only role seems to be to act as fodder for other species. It is an inglorious yet very essential part they play in the natural economy, converting either vegetation or small animal life into bulk protein —for the benefit of other fishes.

Piratical relative

There is, in fact, another species closely related to the troutperches which preys enough on other fishes to be called the pirateperch. Except that it has a deeper body and a more square-ended tail, the pirateperch looks very like the troutperch, but it has no adipose fin. It also is small, up to 5 in. long, and is olive green to brown with dark spots and blotches, usually in rows along the body, and yellowish brown on the underside. Pirateperch live in the eastern United States, from New York to Texas, in streams and standing waters. They are said

to be very quarrelsome, both with fishes of other species and with members of their own species. This is largely because they have a strong territorial drive. The pirateperch prefers waters with muddy beds, where there is debris and rotting leaves, under which it can hide, darting out to take a worm, insect larva or small fish, or to drive away an intruder.

Fat fin mystery

In the salmon, trout and other members of the salmon family the second dorsal fin has been modified to what is called an adipose fin. This is a small flap made up of fatty tissue covered by skin, which lacks fin rays or any other supporting skeleton. An adipose fin is also found in some of the large freshwater family of characins (p 415) and also in the majority of catfishes. In some species it is small, in others large. In the armoured catfishes (p 394) it has a strong spine in front. Conjecture surrounds the function of this small, fatty tag. We know the front dorsal fin of a salmon or trout prevents the fish from rolling and yawing as it moves forward. The pectoral fins, which prevent pitching as well as rolling, are used in turning and, with the pelvic fins, are used for braking. The tail fin helps drive the fish through the water and is used as a rudder. According to some experts the adipose fin has no function. This is hard to believe, but to say what its function might be is even harder.

class	**Pisces**
order	**Percopsiformes**
family	**Percopsidae**
genera & species	***Columbia transmontana*** Columbia troutperch **Percopsis omiscomaycus** blunt-nosed troutperch
family	**Aphredoderidae**
genus & species	***Aphredoderus sayanus*** pirateperch

Trumpeter

Trumpeters are odd-looking birds believed to be a link between the rails and the cranes. About the size of a domestic chicken, 28 in. long, they look rather like dumpy cranes with a hunchbacked stance. The legs and neck are fairly long, the head is small and rounded and the bill chicken-like. The wings are rounded and the tail so short that it is hidden under the feathers of the rump. The feathers of the head and neck are short and soft, almost like hair, and those of the body are long and loose like an ostrich's. The plumage is mainly black with a purplish sheen on the neck.

There are three species of trumpeter, all living in the Amazonian region of South America. The common trumpeter is black with grey on the back and ranges from Venezuela and the Guianas to eastern Ecuador and northeastern Brazil. The white-winged trumpeter has white feathers over the rump and lives in Peru and northwest Brazil. The green-winged trumpeter of northern Brazil is black with green on the wings.

△ *In permanent evening dress—the white-winged trumpeter, found in dense South American jungle.*
◁ *The common trumpeter rarely becomes airborne; when in danger it prefers to run, or even swim.*

John Tashjian at San Diego Zoo

The super-chicken

Trumpeters perch but are poor fliers, preferring to run swiftly to evade capture, and they will even swim rather than fly to cross a wide river. They are also rather unwary and because they are good to eat are becoming rarer as human settlement advances into the forest. They still survive in the depths of the Amazon jungles, however, but this means that it is difficult to study them in a natural state, and their habits are not well known. This is the more surprising since we are told that the birds are so easily tamed. The local peoples keep them to protect their poultry; the trumpeters join the chickens and establish themselves at the top of the peck order. Some have been said to have followed their owners around like dogs. A Mr Vosmaer, nearly 200 years ago, wrote: 'Having reared one myself, I had an opportunity of experiencing this. When I opened its cage in the morning, the kind animal hopped round me, expanding both his wings, and trumpeting, as if to wish me good-morning. He showed equal attention when I went out and returned: no sooner did he perceive me at a distance, than he ran to meet me; and even when I happened to be in a boat, and set my foot on shore, he welcomed me with the same compliments, which he reserved for me alone, and never bestowed upon others.'

Voices for contact

Trumpeters live in flocks of up to 200, roosting together in trees. The members of a flock keep in contact with each other by loud, reverberating calls, which start with short notes and end with drawn-out cries. Imitation of these calls is a sure lure for trumpeters. The birds get their name not from these contact calls but from a loud trumpeting which is used when threatening other trumpeters. It is a deep-toned ventriloquistic sound, and trumpeters used as watchdogs call noisily at night at the first sound or sight of an intruder. Close to, the sound seems to come from the depths of the bird's body. An 18th century writer has compared the sound of the trumpeting to the 'lengthened doleful noise which the Dutch bakers make by blowing a glass trumpet, to inform their customers when the bread comes out of the oven.' They also have a quiet call whose function is not known.

Secondhand food

The food of trumpeters is fallen fruits, berries and insects such as ants and flies. They have the habit of following toucans, howler monkeys and coatis, feeding on the fruits that these animals drop from the trees.

Exuberant courtship

In their courtship, trumpeters gather in open spaces and perform energetic dances, leaping and calling, even turning somersaults. These are strange antics for such heavy-looking birds and are possibly an indication of their relationship with the cranes, which also have exuberant dances. The nest is built in a hole or fork of a tree or on the ground at the base of a tree. Up to 10 green eggs are laid but the incubation period is not known. Chicks from nests on the ground start to run about with their parents soon after hatching, and one must presume that they also leave nests in trees when very young, but there is no evidence as to how they manage this.

Formidable opponents

Nothing is known about the enemies of trumpeters in the wild state, but if we can judge from the reports about trumpeters as pets we can assume that they are fairly well able to look after themselves. Those who have kept these birds all agree that they like being petted and stroked over the head and neck. On the other hand, a tame trumpeter which takes a dislike to somebody will actively pursue that person, pecking at his legs, or if it takes a dislike to a domestic cat or dog will drive the animal out of the room whenever it can, and it is said to be capable of putting a medium-sized dog to flight. 'It avoids the bites of its antagonists by rising in the air; and retaliates by violent blows of its bill and nails aimed chiefly at the eyes; and if it gains a superiority, it pursues the victory with the utmost rancour, and, if not taken off will destroy the fugitive.'

Trumpeters' tubes

Several birds have received the name of trumpeter from their loud, reverberating calls. These include the trumpeter swan (p 2328) and the trumpeter manucode *Phonygammus keraudrenii*, an Australian bird-of-paradise. They owe their loud, trombone-like calls to an extremely long windpipe. That of the trumpeter and the trumpeter manucode is coiled under the skin of the breast. Other birds with long windpipes include the whooping crane (p 562), whose 5ft windpipe is coiled within the breastbone, and the plains chachalaca *Ortalis vetula*. The windpipe acts as a resonator like an organ pipe and, similarly, the pitch depends on its length and diameter. In chickens it is known that certain muscles shorten the windpipe by as much as one quarter. When these muscles contract the chicken's voice rises.

class	**Aves**		
order	**Gruiformes**		
family	**Psophiidae**		
genus & species	*Psophia crepitans* common trumpeter		
	P. leucoptera white-winged trumpeter		
	P. viridis green-winged trumpeter		

Trunkfish

The trunkfishes are the nearest we have to fishes masquerading as turtles. They are also known as boxfishes and cofferfishes because their bodies are enclosed within bony boxes made up of 6-sided bony plates fitting closely into one another, leaving only the tail unarmoured. Inside, the backbone is short with only 14 vertebrae between the skull and the beginning of the tail, all joined in a compact manner.

A typical trunkfish has a more or less conical head, the face sloping down at a steep angle to the small mouth, which is armed with strong crushing teeth. The eyes are large and there is only a small opening from the gill chamber. The length of a trunkfish seldom exceeds 1 ft. The single dorsal fin and the anal fin are fairly large, as are the pectoral fins, but there are no pelvic fins. The fleshy, naked tail ending in a large fanlike tail fin projects backwards from the bony box and, except for the other fins, is the only part capable of movement. The box enclosing the body is flat on the undersurface and it may be 3-, 4- or 5-sided in cross section, and one or more of its edges may be armed with strong spines.

Trunkfishes live at or near the bottom of warm waters, especially in tropical seas, all round the world.

Jane Burton/Photo Res

ES Hobson

Geometrical fishes: a comparison between the fishes above and opposite will show the 3- and 4-faced arrangements of trunkfish armour. These arrangements vary according to species and serve as a rough means of classification.

△ Its transparent, fan-shaped fins beating rapidly, the cumbersome body of a smooth trunkfish moves slowly forwards. Unlike most fish, trunkfishes swim almost entirely by just a rapid beating of their fins.

◁ Passing beauty: **Ostracion meleagris** in the Hawaii reef. Like other trunkfishes, it can adopt a variety of colour schemes. The sexes and young of the same species are often quite differently patterned and coloured.

▷ Front elevation: also known as boxfishes or cofferfishes, trunkfishes such as this **Lactophrys tricornis** are indeed like bony boxes. The tiny mouth is deceptive; it is armed with teeth perfectly capable of biting off coral chunks.

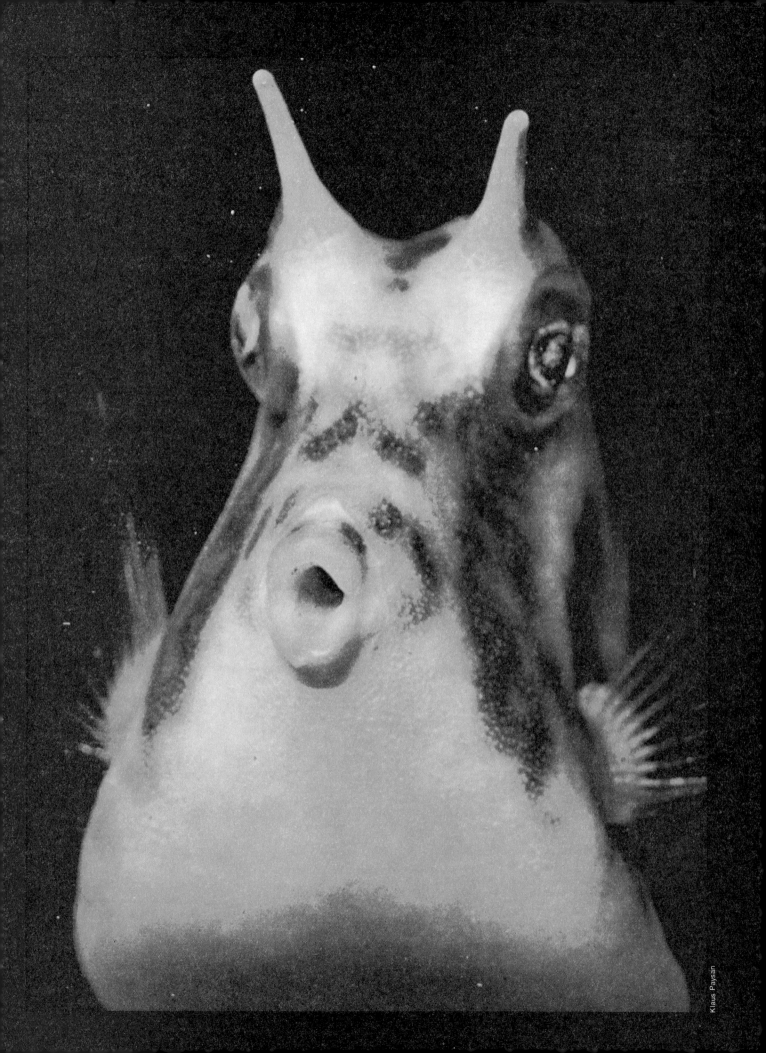

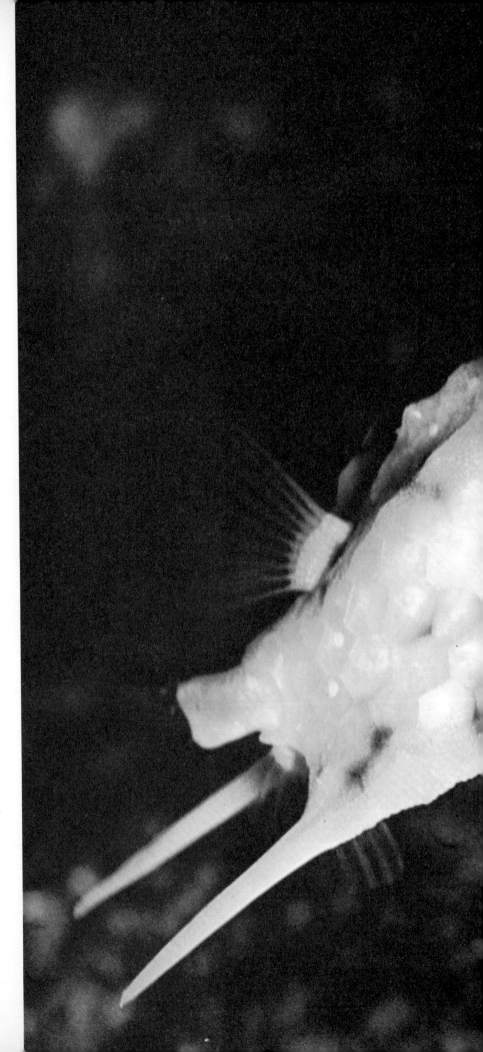

Puffing billys of the sea

Like tortoises on land, trunkfishes are slow moving, and for much the same reasons. The normal fish swims by strong side to side movements of the whole body and, more especially, by the muscular tail. A trunkfish can move its tail only to a small extent. Its swimming is like a small boat being propelled by a single oar sculling from the stern. The only difference is that the hydrodynamic principles are more complex in the fish because the tail is flexible. The main swimming force is produced by side to side movements of the dorsal and anal fins, aided by the pectoral fins. A trunkfish is the very opposite of being streamlined—in fact the flat faces must create considerable resistance to progress—and when swimming it moves its fins very rapidly, giving the impression of a great expenditure of energy with only a little gain in forward movement.

Confusion of colours

Rapid movement is not necessary for so heavily armoured a fish, which can also rely on its colour and colour changes for security, and on its ability to poison other fishes. A common trunkfish found in the seas on both sides of the tropical Atlantic is the cowfish, so named because it has two sharp, forward-pointing spines on the forehead, rather like the horns of a cow. It is pale green in colour, marked with blue spots and lines, but it can change this to yellow with blue spots or brown with a network of light blue markings, or even to pure white. The colours also differ between the sexes. The 4-sided blue trunkfish of the Indo-Pacific is an example. The females and the young fish are purplish blue with numerous small white spots scattered thickly and evenly over the whole body. The male is very different, being purplish blue with a pale blue network except for the flat upper surface, which is a brownish purple with small white dots with a brick-red border. Even the eyes differ: in the females and young fish they are blue, in the males they have a red border.

Unhealthy neighbour

It has been suggested that the gaudy colours act as warning colours, advertising to possible enemies that trunkfishes do not depend entirely on their armour but have other undesirable qualities. We do not know yet exactly how it is used, but we do know that trunkfishes can give out a poison. When one of them is placed in an aquarium it is not long before the other fishes begin to show signs of distress, coming to the surface to gulp air, and dying soon afterwards. The only fishes not affected are tough characters such as moray eels, the large groupers, and other trunkfishes. The poison persists even after the trunkfish have been removed.

Eating hard tack

Trunkfishes live among the corals, which they search for food, biting off pieces of coral to digest the polyps. At the same time, in biting pieces from the coral, they expose worms and other small invertebrates sheltering in it. Some trunkfishes use their spout-like snouts to blow jets of water at the sandy bottom to uncover and dislodge worms, molluscs and small crustaceans, which they immediately snap up.

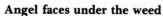

Angel faces under the weed

The breeding habits of the cowfish of tropical American waters are probably typical of the whole family. It lays buoyant eggs, $\frac{1}{32}$ in. diameter, which hatch in 2–3 days. The larvae begin to develop the hard cover in about a week and they become somewhat rounded in shape, and it is only as the young fishes mature that the box-like edges to the body become sharply defined. During the early stages of life young trunkfishes shelter under clumps of floating seaweed. Their rounded shape has earned them, in the United States, the name of dingleberries. At this stage they seem to have rather cherubic faces, with their large eyes, small mouths and what look like puffed cheeks.

Novel seafood

The heaviest mortality among trunkfishes is in the early stages, when eggs, larvae and young fishes are often eaten. Once they reach maturity their protective boxes, and in some species the poison they give out, deter predators. Also, being so slow, they lack the large muscles that make the flesh of other fishes attractive. Yet trunkfishes are eaten, even by human beings, and in some places are regarded as a delicacy. They are cooked in their own boxes, and some people of the South Pacific are said to 'roast them like chestnuts'. There are, nevertheless, other opinions, one of which is that what little flesh there is cannot be praised for its flavour, although the liver is proportionately quite large and oily.

class	**Pisces**
order	**Tetraodontiformes**
family	**Ostraciontidae**
genera & species	***Lactophrys bicaudalis*** *large spotted trunkfish* **L. quadricornis** *cowfish* ***Ostracion lentiginosus*** *blue trunkfish* *others*

◁ *Always in shape, the complete covering of interlocking hexagonal plates of* **O. cornutus** *forms a rigid protective shield over the whole of the body except the flexible tail.*

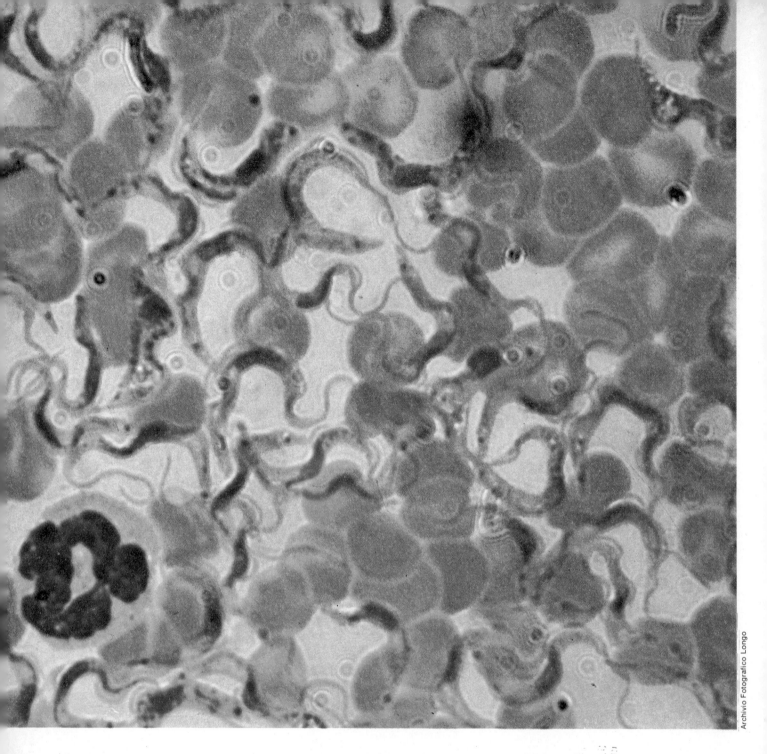

Trypanosome

Trypanosomes are the parasitic protistans responsible for Chagas' disease of Central and South America, African sleeping sickness, and for other diseases of animals. Most of them are transmitted by insects. A trypanosome is typically a long, thin, spindle-shaped, actively wriggling single cell that has a central nucleus and propels itself through blood plasma or other fluids by means of a flagellum. Although it projects from the front of the body, the flagellum has its base near the hind end and is enclosed along the intervening length by a fold of cuticle to form the so-called 'undulating membrane'. Trypanosomes are usually between 0·01 and 0·04

*mm long, although some found in fish and cattle exceed 0·1 mm in length and are visible to the naked eye. They are notoriously variable in form and at some stages in their life cycles the bases of their flagella may lie further forward, so the undulating membrane is short or even absent. A more rounded non-motile form, in which all but the basal structures of the flagellum are lost, is adopted when the parasite is inside a cell, usually in the insect host. This leishmanial form is named after its resemblance to **Leishmania**, a related protistan transmitted by sandflies and responsible for oriental sore and kala-azar. The family to which **Trypanosoma** and **Leishmania** belong also includes other parasites. Some of these live only in the alimentary tracts of insects.*

African diseases

African sleeping sickness is transmitted by the blood-sucking tsetse fly, *Glossina*. The trypanosomes are sucked up through the insect's proboscis and after two or more weeks in the intestine they migrate to the salivary glands. Man is infected by saliva being injected when the tsetse fly takes a meal. The trypanosomes first circulate in the blood plasma then enter lymph nodes, the spleen and the central nervous system. In both kinds of host, human and insect, the parasites multiply asexually by binary fission. That is, they divide into two by a longitudinal division of the cell. There are two kinds of sleeping sickness: the Gambian, or chronic form, caused by *T. gambiense*, occurring particularly in West Africa between 15 degrees North and South, where it is centred on the River Congo and its tributaries, and the Rhodesian form, due to

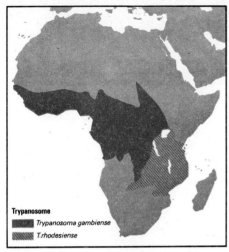

Trypanosome
▓ *Trypanosoma gambiense*
▨ *T. rhodesiense*

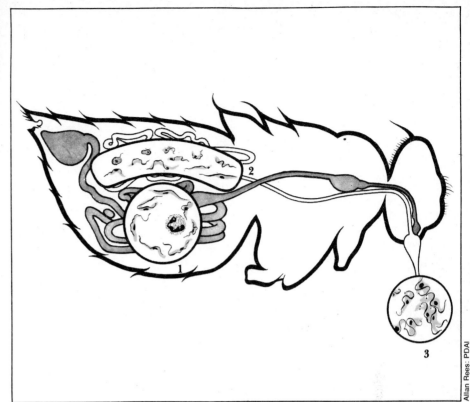

Allan Rees: PDAI

△ *Distribution of two trypanosomes pathological to man—their ranges overlap slightly.*
◁ *Invaders: A human blood smear containing masses of slender* **Trypanosoma rhodesiense**. *Sleeping sickness is caused by the trypanosomes invading the cerebrospinal fluid around the brain.*
▷ *Development of 'tryps' in the tsetse fly.*
1 Long slender forms in the midgut pass to the salivary glands via the hypopharynx.
2 Development of crithidial and later infective 'tryps' in the salivary glands.
3 Inoculation of infective 'tryps'.

T. rhodesiense, almost confined to the high tablelands of southeastern Africa.

Whereas the Rhodesian form is usually fatal within a year, death from the other does not usually occur for several years. Indeed, though usually very unpleasant, it can continue for years without the appearance of any clinical symptoms. Despite these differences, the two parasites look alike. *T. rhodesiense* is moreover probably just a race of *T. brucei* which causes nagana in cattle and also infects pigs and dogs. The normal hosts of this last-named species, to which man is immune, are antelopes, though it causes them little harm. Antelopes are also important as a reservoir for *T. rhodesiense.* The distribution of sleeping sickness in Africa corresponds virtually to the distribution of tsetse fly and it is likely that the distribution of the fly has had a major influence in the past on the growth and spread of civilization. The former prevalence of nagana may likewise have inhibited the exploitation of cattle for load pulling (see p 1168). Fossil tsetse flies have been found in North America, and it is just as well that they died out long before the arrival of infected slaves from Africa. Control of tsetse flies is difficult; the larval stages, usually vulnerable in insects, are difficult to attack since the females carry the larvae until the pupal stage is reached.

South American diseases
Chagas' disease may become fatal within weeks or it may persist for many years, sometimes without symptoms. As much as half the population may be infected in parts of South and Central America. Children under three years old are particularly susceptible. Armadillos form an important reservoir for the parasite *T. cruzi,* and opossums, rodents, cats, dogs and bats are also infected. Transmission is by blood-sucking bugs. Almost all of these bugs may be infected, whereas only a small proportion of tsetse flies are. The trypanosomes reproduce in the intestine of the bug but are not re-injected in saliva as in the tsetse fly. Instead, they fall onto the skin in faeces—the bug tends to defaecate while feeding—and may then be rubbed into the wound. Unusual in that it reproduces in the leishmanial form inside cells of the mammalian host, *T. cruzi* attacks, among other cells, the muscles of the heart. In Central and South America there is another trypanosome transmitted to man by the bug *Rhodnius,* but this one, *T. rangeli,* does not cause disease symptoms.

These four are the only trypanosomes normally found in man, but there are many species found in other vertebrates. Thus a high proportion, possibly as much as 90%, of English sheep become infected with *T. melophagium* through the bites of sheep keds. Birds, too, harbour trypanosomes as do fish, amphibians and reptiles. Transmission is by insects in most cases, but also by leeches in fish. The cause of 'dourine' in horses in southeast Europe, Asia, Africa and parts of North America, *T. equiperdum* is unusual in that the insect host has been dropped, infection being by skin contact during mating.

Darwin a victim?

In 1859, three years after completing his voyage in the *Beagle,* Charles Darwin gave up much of his social life because it tired him too much, and subsequently often suffered from vomiting and gastro-intestinal discomfort, sleeplessness, lassitude and finally heart trouble. Since his doctors could find no organic cause for his ailments, some of his contemporaries ascribed them to hypochondria or the desire to avoid social life. More recent commentators have thought them hysterical or obsessive symptoms due to a subconscious hate and resentment of his father, or considered them a result of remorse for having killed the Heavenly Father with his theories. In 1835, at the eastern foot of the Andes, he suffered an 'attack' of great black Benchuca bugs *Triatoma infestans.* 'It is most disgusting to feel soft wingless insects, about an inch long, crawling over one's body; before sucking they are quite thin, but afterwards round and bloated with blood, and in this state they are easily squashed'. Most of such bugs are infected with *T. cruzi* and it is thought unlikely that Darwin could have escaped infection. Indeed it has been suggested that his death in 1882 was due to Chagas' disease, with which all his symptoms can be accurately matched.

Trypanosomes were first found in 1842, in frogs. The role of trypanosomes and of tsetse flies in nagana was discovered in 1895–7 and in Gambian sleeping sickness in 1901–3, but Chagas' disease was not described until 1909, long after Darwin's death. While carrying out a campaign against malaria, Chagas found trypanosomes in the intestine of a large bug. He sent some insects to Dr Oswaldo Cruz who allowed them to feed on a monkey. Since the monkey subsequently had trypanosomes in its blood, Chagas thought it worthwhile to look for them in man and, after examining many people, he found them in a child, thus giving his name to a disease that has inhibited South American civilisation for centuries.

phylum	**Protozoa**
class	**Mastigophora**
subclass	**Zoomastigina**
order	**Protomonadina**
family	**Trypanosomatidae**

Tsetse fly

*Tsetse is the name, probably of Bantu origin, of a genus of flies, **Glossina**, endemic to Africa south of the Sahara. Tsetse flies are notorious as carriers of the disease known as nagana in cattle and horses and also of sleeping sickness in man. They feed by piercing the skin with their mouthparts and sucking the blood of the mammals, birds and reptiles. Unlike mosquitoes in which only the female sucks blood, both sexes of the tsetse fly feed in this way. About 20 species are known. They are a little larger than houseflies but they differ more especially in the way they fold their wings, scissor-like, over their backs when at rest. **Glossina** belongs to the same family as the housefly and is quite closely related to the common European biting stable fly **Stomoxys**. The mouthparts of both these are modified to varying extents for piercing and sucking, in the same way as those of the tsetse fly.*

Blood-sucking flies

Each species of tsetse fly has its own habitat preference. *Glossina palpalis*, the most important carrier of sleeping sickness, prefers dense forest bordering rivers and lakes. It lives largely on the blood of reptiles such as crocodiles and monitor lizards, and also on that of the marshbuck or sitatunga antelope; it also bites people. In open forest or savannah *G. morsitans* and some related species depend upon game animals for food. These are the carriers of the nagana cattle disease and also of one type—the Rhodesian form—of sleeping sickness.

Almost a marsupial fly

Compared with the breeding habits of other insects, those of the tsetse fly are peculiar. Most insects lay large numbers of eggs to compensate for the heavy mortality suffered by their young, which are usually larvae, fending entirely for themselves, without the power of flight to escape from their enemies. The tsetse flies produce their offspring rather as the mammals do. The female develops only one egg at a time and it hatches inside her body. The larva stays inside the mother and is nourished by a secretion produced by glands which open by a nipple near the larva's mouth. They are, in effect, milk glands. The female maintains the supply of this fluid by constantly taking meals of blood. The larva breathes by means of a pair of black knobs which reach to the exterior through the opening of the female fly's oviduct. When it is fully grown the larva is extruded or 'born'; it falls to the ground and immediately pupates in the soil. A female tsetse fly may live for about 6 months and give birth to not more than 12 larvae during her life. This breeding rate is slower than that of the rabbit!

Tsetse flies and disease

Sleeping sickness is a terrible disease which runs a slow course, from a few months up to several years, and ends in coma and death. It is caused by infection from single-celled organisms, or protistans, known as trypanosomes (p 2478). The transmission of the disease is cyclical. That is to say, the trypanosome undergoes part of its cycle of development in the blood of the vertebrate host and another part in the fly. There are two distinct forms of sleeping sickness. That known as the Gambian form is caused by *Trypanosoma gambiense*, carried mainly by *Glossina palpalis*, and the Rhodesian form, caused by *Trypanosoma rhodesiense*, which is conveyed mainly by *Glossina morsitans*. Rhodesian sleeping sickness first appeared in 1909 in Rhodesia and is more severe, often causing death in a few months.

Effective control

Gambian sleeping sickness can be controlled by felling riverside vegetation or by catching and trapping the flies in paths and clearings. The disease retreats as a matter of course as the increase of human population leads to agriculture replacing waterside forest. As tsetse flies find their victims by sight, dark-coloured models of large mammals, crudely made and therefore cheap to set up, can be used to lure them into open country. They settle on the model and can then be destroyed. They can also be persuaded to deposit their larvae on prepared sites where the pupae can then be destroyed. The flies are attracted by dark colours, while white clothing is effective in repelling them. Fly screens on buildings, vehicles and river boats are also useful. The disease can be cured if diagnosed in good time, and several months protection against infection can be given by injection of a drug called pentamodine. In Rhodesia, wholesale slaughter of game animals has, not surprisingly, been effective in controlling the Rhodesian sleeping sickness.

The cattle disease nagana is far more difficult to control. Several kinds of trypanosomes are involved, *Trypanosoma brucei* and *T. congolense* are the most frequent, being carried by several species of tsetse flies which attack a great variety of animals, birds and reptiles. In these circumstances extermination of wildlife is impracticable as well as being horrible to contemplate.

▽ *Before: **Glossina morsitans** inserts its proboscis into a man's arm ...* ▷ ▽ *and after: gorged with blood. Tracheae show through distended abdomen.*

Why they walked

In the early exploration of Africa by white men it was not always possible to use horses or mules for transport. The familiar picture is of the white explorer walking in front, followed by a long string of porters with boxes and bundles on their heads. This was because of the tsetse fly. Moreover, the impossibility of keeping cattle in large areas of Africa has led to their remaining unpopulated by people to whom cattle are not a food source, but a status symbol.

Efforts are now being made to persuade the pastoral Africans to abandon their miserable cattle and to make intelligent use of the indigenous animals, which are immune to nagana. The deeply rooted tradition of cattle breeding will, however, be hard to eradicate.

A rather unconventional attitude towards the tsetse fly has been well expressed by Professor VB Wigglesworth in his book *The Life of Insects*: 'But there are those who consider the tsetse fly to be the one great saviour of the African soil. By ignorant procedures, or by ruthless exploitation for short-term gains, so much of the soil surface of this planet has been squandered, and vast areas of Africa reduced to semi-desert, that it is possible to regard any insect which bars the way, and conserves the soil for the more enlightened cultivators of the future, as a true friend of man.'

phylum	**Arthropoda**
class	**Insecta**
order	**Diptera**
family	**Muscidae**

Anthony Bannister: NHPA

Marshy savannah — ideal breeding grounds for **Glossina**. *They feed on the abundant game, such as these red lechwe, which become disease reservoirs.*

Anthony Bannister: NHPA

2427

Tuatara

The tuatara is the sole survivor of the beak-heads, a group of very ancient reptiles that flourished during the Age of Reptiles, which lasted from 250 to 70 million years ago, It is the only species of reptile in an order and family of its own. Outwardly it looks like a fairly large lizard but internally it has many fundamental differences from modern lizards. With a length of 2 ft or more, it has a large head with teeth set along the edges of the jaws and a pair of enlarged front upper teeth. The nostrils are double and there is no external opening to the ear. The body and limbs are strongly built and there are powerful sharp claws on the partially webbed, five-toed feet. There is a crest of enlarged spines along the neck, back and tail and the back and sides are covered with small granular scales interspersed with tubercles. The scales of the underparts are larger and more regularly arranged. Like many of the modern lizards the tuatara is able to regenerate its long compressed tail, but not so efficiently. The tuatara's ground colour varies from blackish-brown to olive green or grey with a small yellow spot on each scale, which is brightest after the skin is shed and fades as the animal gets older. The scales of the crest are green.

It is only when the tuatara's anatomy is examined that the distinctions are found that cause it to be placed in a separate order and which make it so interesting to zoologists. In particular the skull is much stronger and firmer than that of other lizards, being more like the skull of a crocodile, with its parts joined together by bony arches. The backbone is primitive in structure, the vertebrae being concave at both ends. The ribs have hook-like processes about halfway along their length for attachment to the muscles. These are found also in birds and some fossil reptiles. The so-called abdominal ribs are well developed, forming a shield made up of several segments. Another unusual feature of the tuatara is the absence of an organ of copulation in the male.

Up to the middle of the 19th century the tuatara was common on the New Zealand mainland but today it is confined to a few rocky islands off the northeast coast of North Island and in Cook Strait between North and South Island. On some of these islands it is now plentiful owing to the New Zealand Government's policy of strict protection.

▽ *Prehistoric portrait: of the many 'beak-heads' — reptiles that flourished 100 million years ago — only the tuatara survives, on a few islands around New Zealand.*

Three-eyed lizards

Perhaps the tuatara's most interesting feature to zoologists is the presence of the third or pineal eye, which is a feature of so many fossil vertebrates. This pineal eye is not, however, peculiar to the beak-heads; it is shared with many other species of lizards but it is better developed in the adult tuatara than in any other animal. Its presence in many embryos confused early ideas on evolution's relation to embryology. It is situated on the top of the brain, with a hole in the skull just above it, and has the vestiges of a lens and retina but no iris. It connects with a glandular body in the brain, but in adults the skin thickens over the opening in the skull and it is unlikely that any light from outside is conducted to the brain. The pineal eye was probably an important sense organ in some of the earlier reptiles but it is not known for sure what function it serves in the tuatara.

One breath an hour

The tuatara may dig its own burrow or share one with a petrel. As far as is known the tuatara lives only on islands where the top soil has been so manured and worked over by these birds' numerous burrows that there is a layer of loose upper soil 18–24 in. deep. The tuatara can often be seen basking in the sun in the morning or evening but spends most of the day in its burrow, coming out to hunt for food only at night. It is active at quite low temperatures, sometimes as low as 11°C/52°F, the lowest temperature recorded for any reptile activity. Its rate of metabolism is very low; the normal rate of breathing even when it is moving about is only one breath per seven seconds, but it can go for at least an hour without a breath.

Although good-tempered when handled gently, a tuatara will scratch and bite in self-defence. Its voice is a harsh croak like that of a frog.

Not such a happy pair

The tuatara's diet consists largely of spiders, crickets, beetles and other insects, although snails and earthworms are also taken. Contrary to the popular image of bird and reptile living amicably together, the tuatara sometimes eats petrel eggs and chicks, even an occasional adult bird.

Unusually long gestation

Nothing is known of the courtship habits of the tuatara. Pairing occurs during January but the sperm are stored in the female's body until the following September or October when 5–15 white, oval, hard-shelled eggs are laid in a shallow depression in the ground which has been scooped out by the female, and covered over with earth. The eggs receive no attention from either parent and do not hatch out until 12–15 months later, the longest incubation period known for any reptile. The young tuataras, which

are brownish pink in colour, break the shells of their eggs and dig their way to the surface. They are about 4½ in. long at this stage but their growth rate is very slow and they do not breed until they are over 20 years old, and they continue to grow until they are 50.

The tuatara has been kept in captivity on a number of occasions, one specimen in New Zealand having been kept for over 50 years. In the wild it lives to well over 50 years, and some claim that it may live to be over 100.

Island sanctuaries

The tuatara probably became extinct on the mainland of New Zealand because it was preyed upon by the many rodents, feral cats and pigs introduced by the English immigrants to New Zealand and which now inhabit the bush. These predators are not present on the islands to which the tuatara is now confined and it can consequently live and breed freely with little disturbance.

Dinosaur contemporary

The beak-heads flourished during the Age of Reptiles, along with the earliest turtles and long before the great dinosaurs trod the earth. They evolved into a remarkable variety of forms which are known from fossils found in many parts of the world. Some of these were larger than the tuatara as we know it today but none reached a length of more than 5–6 ft. After the Jurassic period most of the beak-heads became extinct, the tuatara being the only member of the group to survive until today. It was first named by Dr John Edward Gray of the British Museum, from a specimen received there in 1831, who thought it was merely a new species of lizard. It was not until 1867 that his successor at the Museum, Dr Albert Günter, realised that the animal was no ordinary lizard but was related to the ancient beak-heads, and was truly a living fossil.

△ *Looking seaward—a tuatara and its young.*
△ ◁ *On guard: a tuatara outside its burrow, which it shares with various species of shearwaters. The islands on which the tuatara lives have a remarkable soil and vegetation. Beneath a canopy of low trees of the genus* **Coprosoma** *is a deep layer of soft humus. This is mainly maintained by the burrowing activities of the shearwaters which mix leaves, twigs and excreta into an even composition. The islands' vegetation has suffered due to the introduction of goats, but fortunately their numbers have now been checked.*

class	**Reptilia**
order	**Rhynchocephalia**
family	**Sphenodontidae**
genus & species	*Sphenodon punctatus*

Tubenose

The tubenose looks like a living dart. On the one hand, it is closely related to the sticklebacks, on the other, to half a dozen other fishes with tubelike snouts. It is a marine fish living off the Pacific coast of North America from Alaska to California, at depths of down to 100 ft, but mostly at a depth of 30–40 ft. A tubenose is slender, up to 6½ in. long, its head making up about 1¼ in. of this. There is a single triangular dorsal fin just in front of the slender tail which ends in a small, slightly forked tailfin. A row of 25 small spines runs from just behind the head to the leading edge of the dorsal fin. The anal fin is opposite the dorsal and is like it in shape and size. The very small pelvic fins lie almost under the throat, level with the pectoral fins. The body is coloured olive green on the back shading to silvery on the flanks and is whitish on the belly.

Monster shoals

Tubenoses spend all their lives in shoals or schools, which are often very large. The outstanding record is one taken in November 1950 off Santa Rosa Island, southern California, where biologists of the Fish and Game Commission measured a tubenose shoal ¼ mile in diameter, entirely filling the water between 30 and 70 ft depth. Any estimate of the number of fishes in this shoal must be largely speculation, but it could have been between 200 and 600 million, depending on how closely the fishes were arranged in the shoal. It is of interest to recall another huge shoal, comparable in proportions, of the related 3-spined stickleback (p 2272) in an English river.

Only small food is taken, by sucking into the tubelike mouth. It includes amphipods, opossum shrimps, the zoea larvae of crabs and fish larvae.

Attentive father

Tubenoses are unusual in that they spawn throughout the year. The male builds a nest among the young growths at the base of a giant kelp, using sticky threads given out from his kidneys, in the manner of sticklebacks. He then entices the female to the nest to lay her orange coloured, translucent eggs. These hatch after 2–3 weeks, during which time the male guards the nest, driving away intruders. He also aerates the eggs by fanning currents of water through the nest with his fins. He does not allow the larvae to leave the nest until they are well developed and are able to form small schools in the quiet waters close to the sea bed, in the shelter of rocks or seaweeds. Tubenoses mature in less than a year.

Fish fodder

The stomach contents of large carnivorous fishes are the chief source of information we have about the enemies of tubenoses. Piecing the story together from these it is clear that at times there are enough tubenoses to serve as the main food for quite a number of predatory fishes.

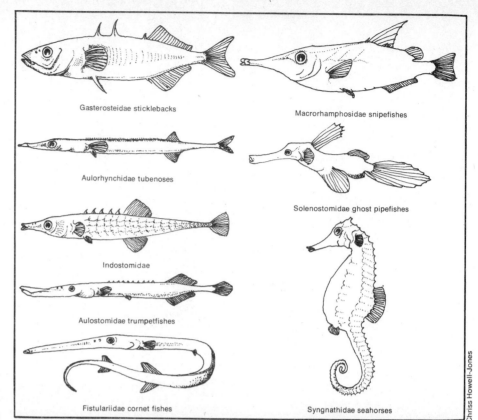

Gasterosteidae sticklebacks

Macrorhamphosidae snipefishes

Aulorhynchidae tubenoses

Solenostomidae ghost pipefishes

Indostomidae

Aulostomidae trumpetfishes

Fistulariidae cornet fishes

Syngnathidae seahorses

Chriss Howell-Jones

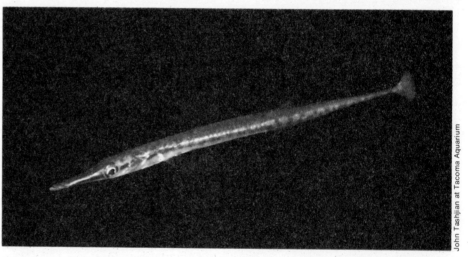

John Tashjian at Tacoma Aquarium

Tubenoses all

There are a number of fishes with tubular mouths. The best known are the pipefishes (p 1771) and the seahorses (p 2066). Related to them are trumpetfishes, family Aulostomidae, and the cornetfishes, family Fistulariidae, both named after the resemblances their mouths show to the relevant musical instruments. The snipefishes, family Macrorhamphosidae, are squat fishes, with the head taking up about a third of the total length, and with the tubular snout recalling the long, slender beak of the bird after which they are named. Shrimpfishes, family Centriscidae (p 2135), are like them but have a transparent body covering, like a shrimp. Then there are the ghost pipefishes, family Solenostomidae, also with a squat body, a flowing tailfin and an even longer tubular snout. Finally, discovered as recently as 1929 in Lake Indawgyi, Upper Burma, and the only freshwater species among them, is

△△ *A series of tubenose relatives to show the range of snout form described in the text.*
△ *Solitary tubenose on the lookout for a meal.*

the fish *Indostomus paradoxus* of the family Indostomidae, which has been described as a cross between a pipefish and a stickleback. Until a few years ago, all these were placed in an order far removed from the tubenose. Now it is realised that they are all closely related, united by many features and showing all intermediate stages from a stickleback to a seahorse. In effect, there is not merely one species, and if justice were done we should call all these fishes tubenoses.

class	**Pisces**
order	**Gasterosteiformes**
family	**Aulorhynchidae**
genera & species	*Aulichthys japonicus* Japan *Aulorhynchus flavidus*

Tubeworm

Many marine worms live in tubes but the one known as the parchment-tube worm, or tubeworm, **Chaetopterus**, is the most remarkable of all. Other tube-dwelling worms use sandgrains or other hard materials to make their tubes. The tubeworm uses only the slime from its own glands to make a tube 15 in. to several feet long and ½ in. diameter. The worm itself, up to 15 in. long, has three distinct parts to its body. The front part carries the mouth, two tentacles, nine pairs of spear-shaped bristles and, behind these, a pair of wing-like processes that can be brought together at their tips to form a ring that can be pressed against the wall of the tube. Behind this, on the upper surface, is a sucker-like ciliated cup. There is a ciliated groove running from the mouth to the cup. The middle part of the body is made up of five segments carrying three pairs of plate-shaped fans. The end part of the worm, and the longest, is more like the body of a ragworm (p 1901).

Chaetopterus variopedatus is found in all parts of the world, sometimes low down on the shore, more often just below extreme low-tide mark. Where found it is likely to be present in large numbers. In some parts of the world it is especially numerous in the mud near the mouths of estuaries.

◁ The tube of **Chaetopterus variopedatus** slit open to reveal the coiled occupant.

Food conveyor system

The mucous tube of the tubeworm has been described as leathery and parchment-like. Its colour has been given as white, yellow, brown and green. It is U-shaped with only the ends sticking up above the surface of the mud. These two ends are much narrower than the rest of the tube and are about an inch long. They are not conspicuous and can easily be missed, especially when they are among the kelp. As a result, although a great deal has been written about this remarkable tubeworm it is not often found by naturalists.

Except when the worm is moving about in its tube it is anchored to the wall of the tube by suckers on its undersurface. The three pairs of fans are used as paddles to drive water through the tube, bringing in oxygen and carrying away wastes. The current also brings food, which is trapped in a mucous bag. Mucus is given out from the winglike processes. Cilia in the groove carry the mucus back, stretching it like a bag until it reaches the ciliated cup. Since any water entering the tube must pass through this bag any particles will be trapped at its end. There the cilia in the cup roll up the mucus and its contained particles to form a pellet. The action of the cilia in the groove is then reversed and the pellet is carried by them to the mouth where it is swallowed. Another mucous bag is formed, more particles accumulate in it and another pellet is rolled and passed back to the mouth. The fans keep beating except when a pellet is being passed to the mouth. This has been timed on several occasions: the interval averages 18 minutes.

Fine particulate feeder

Although we can say the tubeworm feeds on particles it is less easy to say what the particles may be. They may include bacteria as well as fine particles of dead and decaying plant and animal matter. It feeds only while it is in a tube. The moment it is taken out it stops feeding, which makes it hard to find out the nature of its food except by inference. A related species *Mesochaetopterus rickettsi*, for example, lives in a blind tube up to 8 ft long that goes down 4 ft into the sand. One suggestion is that the blind end of the tube contains a well of stagnant water where bacteria will breed. In this species there is no mucous bag but a string of mucus which is given off from the rear part of the body and continuously drawn along to the mouth. It could be carrying bacteria with it. In other related species there is evidence that particles of dead plants and animals make up the food.

Orthodox life history

As with other marine tube-dwelling worms the ova and sperms are shed into the sea, where fertilisation takes place. When one worm spawns it liberates a chemical into the water which sets off the other worms around, so they all spawn together. From the fertilised egg a free-swimming larva develops and although further details of the larval development are not known, we can say that the first two parts of the young worm develop the most rapidly, and the rear end is at first short with only a few tail segments instead of the 30 seen in the full-grown adult.

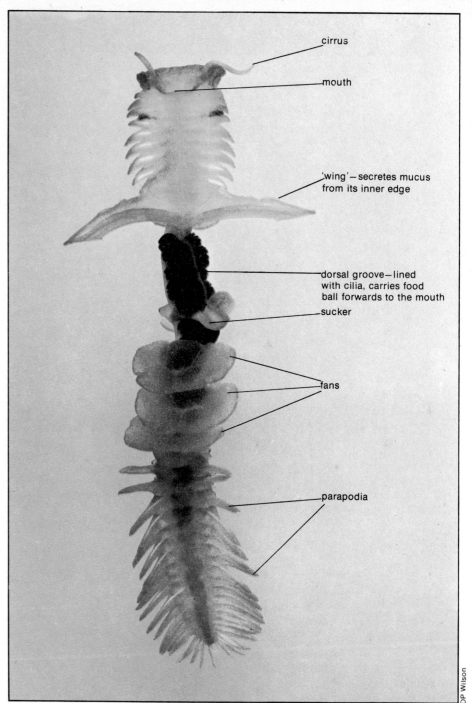

cirrus

mouth

'wing' — secretes mucus from its inner edge

dorsal groove — lined with cilia, carries food ball forwards to the mouth

sucker

fans

parapodia

DP Wilson

Out of its tube: the bizarre form of **Chaetopterus**. *Its body is highly modified for filter feeding.*

Renewing lost parts

The tubeworm sometimes has parts such as the tentacles or the front part of the head bitten off. It can regrow these lost parts, in about 10 – 14 days. It can also regrow the whole head end or most of the tail end. In another instance, a tubeworm which broke up when being handled in the laboratory regrew both a head and a tail end from the middle portion of the three fans.

Puzzling light

As well as its remarkable feeding methods and its powers of regeneration, the tubeworm has set scientists a puzzle which has so far not been solved. The worm stays all the time, once it has left the larval stage, in a tube buried under the mud. Yet the moment it is touched or disturbed it lights up. If it is touched gently only on one part of the body, the light appears only on that part. When touched roughly the light spreads all over its body. Three tubeworms taken from their tubes and put in a dish of water in the laboratory gave enough light 'to read a watch'. The tubeworm has no eyes so cannot use the light. The simplest explanation is that the light is a byproduct of the worm's physiology, and as with other bioluminescent animals may have evolved to get rid of oxygen before animals' breathing became aerobic.

phylum	**Annelida**
class	**Polychaeta**
family	**Chaetopteridae**

Tubifex

*Because **Tubifex**, a small red aquatic worm, is used so much by aquarists as fish food its scientific name has become used as a common name. It is like a slender earthworm, ½—2 in. long, its body cylindrical and divided into many ring-like segments. Four bundles of bristles protrude from each segment, except the first and last, with more than two bristles per bundle. These are moved by muscles and used to grip the mud in crawling and burrowing. As in earthworms, there is a saddle, or clitellum, which is like a cigar band around the body and is involved in reproduction and the formation of egg cocoons.*

*About two dozen species of **Tubifex** occur all around the world and several species are found in Britain. Some live in fresh water and others in the sea, on shore or in shallow water, while a few live in estuaries or other waters of intermediate and fluctuating salinity. Of those living in the brackish water of estuaries, **T. costatus** is essentially marine and **T. tubifex** essentially a freshwater species. The common European species **T. tubifex** is found both in Europe and North America. There are also many related species, those belonging to the genera **Ilyodrilus** and **Peloscolex** being sufficiently like the common species loosely to be called tubifex.*

Mud-grubbing bloodworms

Tubifex worms are characteristic of foul conditions, though not confined to them. They can flourish in water so lacking in oxygen that it supports no other life but sewage fungi. They can be found in sewage filters, in sewage-fouled streams and in the mud of ponds. The mud of the Thames at low tide in London may be reddened by countless *Tubifex*, together with another red worm *Limnodrilus* of the same family, distinguished by orange-yellow stripes on its rear end. There may be tens of thousands to a square yard of mud. Another animal occurring in water nearly as low in oxygen as that which *Tubifex* can stand is the blood red larva of the midge, *Chironomus*. The colour of *Chironomus* and *Tubifex*, both referred to sometimes as 'bloodworms' and sometimes occurring together, is due to haemoglobin in their blood. This helps them to make the best use of what oxygen there is available. *Tubifex* lives with its head end downward in the mud, and digesting from it bacteria and decayed organic matter. The worm is partly enclosed in a projecting, chimney-like tube of mud and mucus, but the tail end extends free in the water, writhing to and fro for much of the time to stir up the water and aid in the absorption of oxygen from it. As the oxygen content of the water falls, so the worm tends to extend more and more of its length from its tube and may even come right out. Any disturbance of the water causes all the tubifex to pop back into the mud. If a number of worms are kept together without mud, they entwine themselves in writhing masses.

Writing in agony? A ball of squirming tubifex worms provide a tasty meal for some guppies.

Jane Burton: Photo Res

Reserve eggs for food

Tubifex is hermaphrodite, the male openings being on the underside of the eleventh segment from the front and the female openings in the groove between that segment and the twelfth. The clitellum is on both those two segments. Pairing tubifex exchange sperms cemented together in spermatophores, which are elongated, glistening, white bodies, up to $\frac{1}{12}$ in. long. The spermatophores pass with the eggs into the cocoon that is secreted by the clitellum and there the cement is dissolved, releasing the sperms to fertilise the eggs. The whitish grey cocoons have a cylindrical neck at each end, are about $\frac{1}{16}$ in. long and are usually oval. The eggs are $\frac{1}{80} — \frac{1}{50}$ in. diameter and there may be 1—17, usually 4—9, in each cocoon. In those cocoons with the most eggs, some may not hatch, but may serve as nourishment for the others. The eggs hatch after 8—56 days. The young worms are ¼ in. long and have 30—35 segments on hatching. There are 112—130 segments in the adult. Sexual maturity is reached in the autumn; cocoons are first seen in November.

Tubifex and its relatives

The great majority of marine worms are polychaetes—on each segment there are many chaetae or bristles. Earthworms are known as oligochaetes, meaning they have few chaetae. The tubifex stands between them, because although it is called an oligochaete it has several bristles in each bundle. It also differs from an earthworm in having a gizzard, only one pair of hearts where the earthworm has five, and in other basic anatomical details.

There are other relatives that burrow in the kind of mud where tubifex is found, or crawl on the seaweeds. Some use mud particles to make tubes, cementing them with slime given out by their bodies. These tubes may be fixed or the worms may be able to carry them around with them. Some of these oligochaetes live on the shore, under stones, in mud or on seaweeds. One freshwater oligochaete *Aulophorus carteri* makes its tubes from the spores of a water fern.

Hoaxing the fishes

Its habit of exposing the hind end of its red body from the mud must at times make tubifex very vulnerable to predators. The foul conditions in which the worm flourishes, however, and which indeed make this habit of exposing the body necessary, do not generally support many other animals, predatory or otherwise. A possible way in which marine worms could gain some protection is suggested by observations of Professor Koenig of Vienna, though the worms in question were not positively identified as *Tubifex*. Having collected some sand from the Mediterranean coast near Portofino for an aquarium, Professor Koenig later saw a beautiful red sea anemone sitting in the aquarium. The following day there were two, but half the size. On closer observation, the anemones proved to be nothing of the kind, but instead to be collections of tubifex-like worms, which were able to creep in a chain through the sand and reassemble at the surface elsewhere as new 'anemones'. Small fish, normally fond of worms, clearly avoided swimming within their reach, just as they might avoid real anemones.

phylum	**Annelida**
class	**Oligochaeta**
order	**Plesiopora plesiothecata**
family	**Tubificidae**

Tuco-tuco

The tuco-tucos are rodents that are heard more often than they are seen. Their common name is derived from their bell-like call note which comes echoing up from underground. In outward appearances and in their habits they closely resemble the North American pocket gophers (p 1801) although they have no external cheek pouches. Tuco-tucos have a stocky body, 7 — 10 in. long, with a 2 — 4 in. tail. A full-grown adult weighs 7 — 24 oz. The head is large with a blunt snout and strong upper incisors. The external ears are reduced to little more than small folds of skin around small openings on the sides of the head. The neck and limbs are short and muscular with the forelimbs slightly shorter than the hindlimbs. The hindfeet are fringed with long hair, the forefeet have strong claws used in burrowing which are longer than the toes. The fur varies in length and density in the various species and the colour ranges from dark brown to a creamy buff.

The 50 species differ in only minor points of appearance and habits and many of them may be no more than local races. One species **Ctenomys lewisi** tunnels in the banks of streams and it is thought that it may be partly aquatic. Tuco-tucos are found in tropical to subarctic regions from southern Peru to Tierra del Fuego, the largest numbers occurring in Argentina. In some areas they are becoming scarce, especially in regions where the land has been fenced in for sheep-raising.

Long shallow tunnels

The tuco-tuco is a burrower preferring dry sandy soil but it is found in many different types of habitat from coastal regions and plains to forests and high plateaux. It sometimes lives in large colonies, where several adult females may occupy the same burrow. In excavating their long tunnels these rodents are said to use their head, chest and forefeet to loosen the soil, then their hindfeet to throw it out backwards. The incisors are unusually broad and may possibly be used in digging. The courses of the tunnels are marked by heaps of loose soil like molehills—indeed, in some regions the animal is called the South American mole rat. Vicunas are often seen dust-bathing in sand thrown up by the burrowing. The tunnels are fairly shallow, never more than a foot below the surface, and have chambers for food storage and nesting. They are sometimes so extensive that a large area of land may become undermined, making horse-riding dangerous and hindering the movement of machinery.

Tuco-tucos are most active early in the morning and again late in the afternoon, spending most of the rest of the day in their burrows. Before coming out to feed they can look out of the entrance to see if there is any danger without showing themselves, as their eyes are almost level with the top of the head. When feeding they seldom wander more than a few feet from their burrows. Consequently they are seldom seen by the local inhabitants although their calls are often heard. They have very good eyesight, unlike gophers, and some species are said to be able to distinguish a moving human being as much as 50 yds away. They groom themselves to remove the loose sand from their fur by combing with the stiff bristles that grow near the bases of the hind claws.

In some areas guinea pigs and lizards share the burrows with the tuco-tucos and when they leave mice and lizards often take them over.

Tuco-tucos have been kept successfully in captivity but skin infection often causes a high mortality. *C. torquatus* is often used for physiological research.

Greedy hoarders

Tuco-tucos feed entirely on plant foods such as grass, tubers, roots and stems. They collect these and store them in special chambers in their burrows although all of them may not be eaten. They do not seem to need drinking water, probably obtaining enough moisture from their food. One species *C. opimus* in southern Peru, feeds almost entirely on spiny grass, *Festuca orthophylla*.

Variable mating season

There is little information on the breeding habits of many of the species in the wild. The gestation period in *C. torquatus* is 103 — 107 days and in all species there is one litter a year of 1 — 5 young. They are born in a grass-lined nest at the bottom of the tunnel. The mating season varies in different regions but occurs mainly in the wet season when plant food is abundant. In *C. peruanus* the young are well-developed at birth, able to leave the nest, and feed on green vegetation almost immediately. They can also give the adult call. They are able to breed before they are a year old but seldom live longer than three years in the wild. South American foxes, hog-nosed skunks, wild cats and hawks all prey on the tuco-tuco.

Harmonious blacksmiths

The name of these rodents may be spelt tuco-tuco, tucu-tucu, or tucu-tuco because, we are told, its calls sound like a series of *tuc-tuc-tuc* sounds. WH Hudson, who wrote so eloquently about natural history in South America, gives us a more vivid description: 'not seen, but heard; for all day long and all night sounds its voice, resonant and loud, like a succession of blows from a hammer; as if a company of gnomes were toiling far down underfoot, beating on their anvils, first with strong, measured strokes, then with lighter and faster, and with a swing and rhythm as if the little men were beating in time to some rude chant unheard above the surface.'

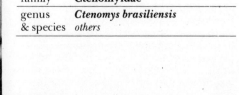

class	**Mammalia**
order	**Rodentia**
family	**Ctenomyidae**
genus & species	*Ctenomys brasiliensis* *others*

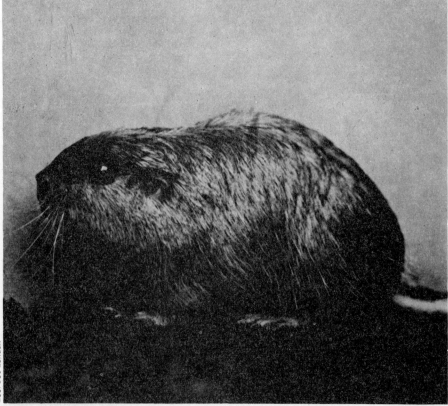

◁ *Stay at home rodent: the tuco-tuco is shy and reticent, rarely straying far from its burrow. As its eyes are near the top of its head it can see if danger exists without leaving its hole.*

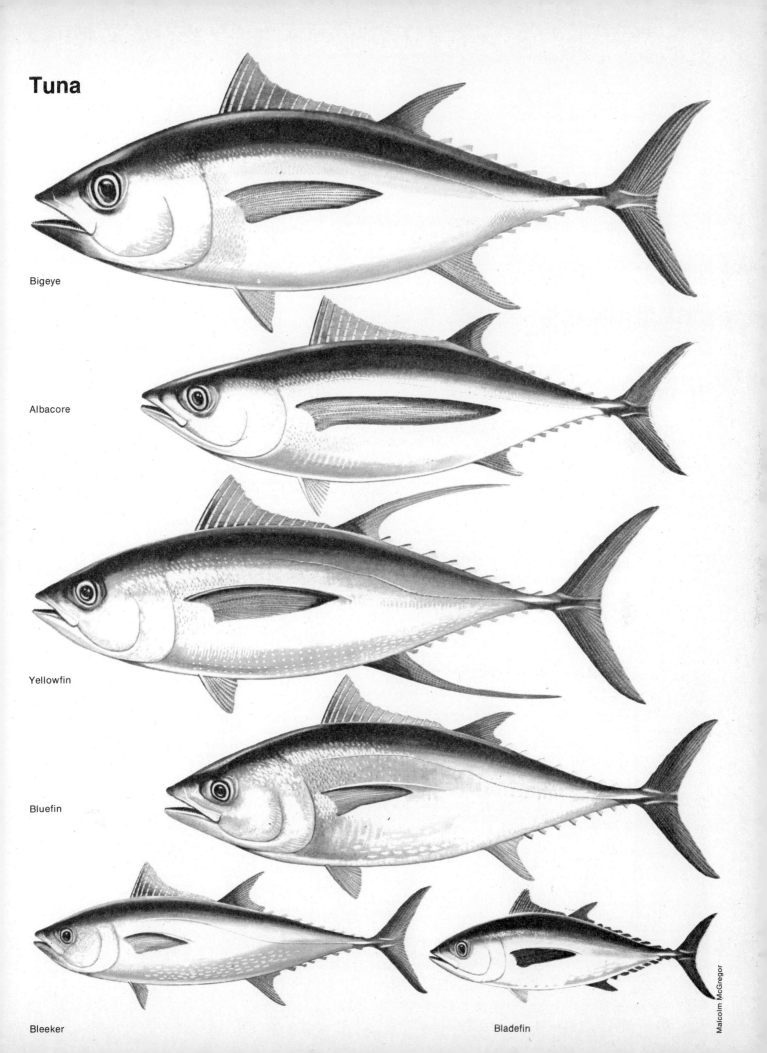

Tuna

Bigeye

Albacore

Yellowfin

Bluefin

Bleeker

Bladefin

Malcolm McGregor

Follow the leader: a shoal of bluefin tuna migrate northward through the Florida-Bermuda channel.

Tuna

*Although the name 'tunny' was first used in England—from the Latin **thunnus**—at least as early as the 15th century, and the Spanish word tuna did not come into general use until the beginning of this century, tuna is rapidly becoming the accepted name for this large fish.*

The tunny or bluefin tuna of the Mediterranean is said to reach 14 ft long and weigh 1 800 lb, but few exceed 8 ft in length. It has a sleek streamlined shape with a large head and mouth, and large eyes. The first dorsal fin is spiny and close behind it is a smaller soft-rayed second dorsal fin. The anal fin is of similar shape and size as the second dorsal, and behind these two, reaching to the crescentically forked tail, are finlets, nine on the upper and eight on the lower surface of the tail. The pectoral fins are medium sized, as are the pelvic fins, which are level with the pectorals. The back is dark blue, the flanks white with silvery spots and the belly white. The fins are dark blue to black except for the reddish brown second dorsal and the yellowish anal fin and finlets. There are three keels on each side at the base of the tailfin.

The bluefin is found on both sides of the North Atlantic as far north as Iceland.

Segregated by size

Tuna are oceanic fishes that sometimes come inshore but apparently never enter rivers. They move about in shoals in which individual fishes are all about the same size. The smaller tuna make up the largest shoals; the larger the tuna the smaller the shoal, and the really large indivuals are more or less solitary. They swim near the surface in summer but are found between 100 and 600 ft in winter. Tuna are strongly migratory, their movements being linked with those of the fishes on which they feed and also on the

temperature of the water. They are intolerant of temperatures below $10-12°C/50-54°F$, so although they move into northern waters in summer they migrate back to warmer seas in autumn. A cold summer will limit the northward migrations. There also seem to be movements across the Atlantic. Tuna tagged off Martha's Vineyard, Massachusetts in July 1954 were caught in the Bay of Biscay five years later and occasionally individuals from American waters turn up off the coasts of Norway. Two tagged off Florida in September and October 1951 were caught off Bergen, Norway 120 days later, having travelled 4 500 miles.

Tuna, like their relative the mackerel, swim with the mouth slightly open so that their forward movement forces water across the gills. Their oxygen requirements are high because of their great muscular activity which depends on a correspondingly abundant supply of relatively warm blood. Because of this high oxygen requirement they swim more or less continuously. Tuna are believed to reach speeds of up to 50 mph.

Feeding frenzy

Very young tuna feed largely on crustaceans especially euphausians but later they eat mainly shoaling fishes such as herring, mackerel, sprats, whiting, flying fishes and sand eels. They also eat some squid and cuttlefish. When a tunny shoal meets a shoal of food fishes it is seized with what has been called a feeding frenzy. It charges through, the tunny twisting and turning, often breaking the surface, and sometimes leaping clear of the water. The commotion usually attracts flocks of seabirds to feed on the smaller fishes that are driven to the surface.

Soon put on weight

Spawning takes place in the Mediterranean and to the southwest of Spain in June and July and off Florida and the Bahamas in May and June. The eggs are small and float near the surface. They hatch in about 2 days, the newly hatched larvae being less than $\frac{1}{4}$ in. long. The baby fishes grow quickly reaching a weight of 1 lb in 3 months. At a year old

they weigh 10 lb, at 2 years 21 lb, 35 lb at 3 years and 56 lb at 4 years of age. At 13 years of age they reach a length of 8 ft and weigh 440 lb. The two tagged at Martha's Vineyard were 18 lb and nearly two years old, and they had reached 150 lb when captured later in the Bay of Biscay, at the age of 7 years.

Ancient fisheries

The many references to the tunny in classical literature show it to have been as important to the Mediterranean peoples as the herring was to the people of northwest Europe. The fisheries have continued through the centuries. Many methods have been used for catching the fish, such as harpoons, baited hooks and nets. The most spectacular are the net fisheries; very long nets are used to intercept migrating shoals and guide them into a final compartment or 'death chamber'. When this is filled with jostling fish the net floor is raised, the surrounding boats close in and the massed fish are clubbed, speared and dragged into the boats. Tuna fishing, or tunny fishing, according to whether it is carried out in American or British waters, has become a popular sport during the last half century. A large fish has been described as 'the tiger of the seas' and 'a living meteor' that strikes like a whirlwind and, played with a rod, will give a man the contest of his life, perhaps towing his boat for hours over a distance of several miles before becoming exhausted. The chief natural enemy is the killer whale.

Wide ranging tunas

There has long been some doubt whether the tuna of the American Atlantic is the same species as the tunny of the European side. They differ slightly in details of anatomy and in the time of the breeding season. Nevertheless, the tendency now is to treat them as separate populations of a single species. Other related species have similar wide distributions. A near relative, the Atlantic albacore, up to 4 ft long and 65 lb weight, with long scythe-like pectoral fins, has its counterpart in the Pacific albacore which ranges from the Pacific coast of North America to Japan and Hawaii. In the yellow-finned albacores or yellow-finned tunas, up to 9 ft long and 400 lb weight, the second dorsal and anal fins are also long and scythe-like. One species ranges across the tropical and subtropical Atlantic and another ranges across the Pacific and into the Indian Ocean. The actual identification of species is difficult because tuna, like many of the large fishes, seldom reach museums, where they can be effectively studied.

class	**Pisces**	
order	**Perciformes**	
family	**Scombridae**	
genus	***Thunnus alalunga*** albacore	
& species	***T. albacares*** *yellowfin*	
	T. atlanticus *bladefin*	
	T. obesus *bigeye*	
	T. thynnus *bluefin*	
	T. tonngol *bleeker*	

Turaco

The turacos, or touracos, some of which are known as louries, go-away birds or plaintain eaters, are lively, fruit-eating birds. Their nearest relatives appear to be non-parasitic cuckoos, such as the couas of Madagascar. There are about 18 species, most of them about 18 in. long, the size of a wood pigeon, but the giant or great blue turaco is 2½ ft long, about the size of a pheasant. The wings are short and rounded and the tail is rather long. The bill is strong and curved. The plumage is usually grey or brown, as in the go-away birds, but some species have considerable amounts of green with red patches on the wings and red, white or other colours on the head. All turacos have crests except for the violet plantain eater which has short, hair-like feathers on the head.

Turacos are confined to Africa south of the Sahara. Some are widely distributed such as the giant turaco of West Africa, Congo and Malawi but a few are very restricted, including the Prince Ruspoli's turaco which lives in a small area of Abyssinia.

Reversible toes for agility

Turacos are found only where there are trees, from the thick evergreen forests, where the giant and blue-crested turacos live, to the dry savannahs of the eastern coast of Africa. The Ruwenzori turaco lives up to 12 000 ft above sea level. The forest-dwelling species have the most green in their plumage while those living in thorn scrub may have none. Thus the forest turacos are well camouflaged, their red wing patches showing only in flight. When disturbed they freeze, becoming completely inconspicuous, then quietly run through the branches, making their way up into the safety of the canopy.

Branches and foliage present no obstacles to turacos because of the peculiar form of their feet. When two toes face forward and two backwards, as in owls and woodpeckers, birds' feet are called zygodactylous. The feet of turacos are semi-zygodactylous; they have a special joint on the outer toe. At rest this toe sticks out sideways but it can be moved either forwards or backwards. This special joint makes it easy for turacos to walk to the tips of the smaller branches, among the leaves and twigs where they hunt for their food.

Turacos are solitary and gather in small groups only where food is abundant. The black-tipped crested turaco roosts huddled in small groups. Turacos are inquisitive and readily approach men or snakes. Their calls are harsh and the go-away birds are named after their cries of 'go-waa'.

▷ Not a feather out of place: an immaculate **Tauraco livingstonii** shines with metallic colour. The coloration of turacos is due to unique pigments; the green comes from tura-coverdin, the red from turacin, both pigments being named after these birds.

Eating poison

The main food of turacos is fruit, which they eat very wastefully, dropping more than they consume. The waste is, however, probably only relative as the fallen fruits are sure to be eaten by other animals. Turacos show definite preferences for certain kinds of fruit. The Knysna lourie is remarkable for eating the poisonous red fruits of a shrub called 'bushman poison'. Shoots and leaves are also eaten and small invertebrates are taken by some turacos. The black-billed or Congo turaco feeds on small snails and the black-tipped crested turaco feeds on invertebrates flushed by driver ants on the forest floor.

Precocious young

The nests of turacos are like those of pigeons: flat platforms of loosely-woven twigs built in dense foliage, usually quite low in the tree. Most of their nesting habits have not been well documented but VGL Van Someren has studied the blue-crested plantain-eater in detail. It has two breeding seasons in each year: April–July and September–January. It appears, however, that each individual nests only once a year. Turacos living near the equator nest all the year round, but elsewhere they generally do so just after the rainy season. The floor of the nest is so thin that the two white eggs can be seen through it. The incubating parent holds its head in such a way as to break the silhouette and so appear less conspicuous. The incubation period is thought to be around 18 days and the fledgling period about a month. The latter is difficult to record because the chicks, which hatch with a covering of black down, leave the nest before they can fly and clamber about using wing claws like those on young hoatzins or mousebirds (p 1079). The chicks are fed on regurgitated fruit.

Unique pigments

The red and green colours in the plumage of turacos are unusual. In most birds green is either produced by the structure of the feather, see fairy bluebird (p 728), or by a mixture of two pigments: brown melanin and a yellow carotenoid. In turacos the green is due to a single green pigment, turacoverdin. The red pigment of the wings and head is called turacin and is found nowhere else in the Animal Kingdom.

Jane Burton: Photo Res

For a long time it has been said that the red pigment runs easily and that the red plumage of turacos fades in the rain. To dispel this belief JP Chapin wore a red turaco feather in his hat for 18 months. If anything the colour became darker because turacin is slowly oxidised in the air. Similarly, in museum specimens the red plumage darkens rather than fades.

This darkening with exposure is unusual. Red pigments tend to run, as is well known in laundries, or fade, as can be seen on posters where red letters disappear even when protected from rain. Perhaps the turacos have the answer the dye manufacturers are seeking.

class	**Aves**
order	**Cuculiformes**
family	**Musophagidae**
genera & species	***Corythaeola cristata*** *giant turaco* ***Musophaga violacea*** *violet plantain eater* ***Ruwenzorornis johnstoni*** *Ruwenzori turaco* ***Tauraco corythaix*** *Knysna lourie* ***T. hartlaubi*** *blue-crested turaco* ***T. macrorhynchus*** *black-tipped crested turaco* ***T. ruspolii*** *Prince Ruspoli's turaco* ***T. schuttii*** *Congo turaco others*

▽ *Poised for takeoff: a startled Donaldson's turaco* **Tauraco leucotis**. △ *Ross's turaco* **Musophaga rossae** *raising its smart crest.*

John Markham

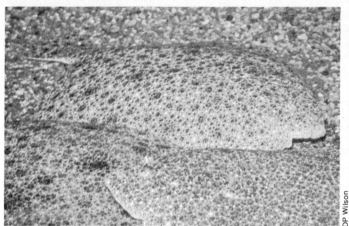
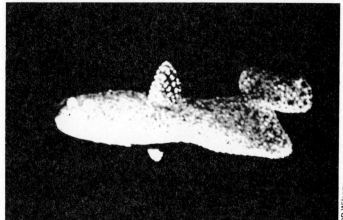

Head to tail turbot, showing both sides of the typical crooked head.

After a propulsive body-ripple, a turbot glides in mid-water.

Turbot

The turbot has the reputation among many people of being the finest flavoured of all sea fishes. Ever since a fisherman presented a very large one to the Emperor Nero, it has had the reputation of growing to a considerable size. It was said there was no dish large enough to take it, and that Nero summoned his senators to gaze on this marvel.

In fact, the turbot grows up to 31 in. long, very rarely reaching 39 in. Its average weight is 25–32 lb with a maximum of 55 lb. Its body is broad and diamond shaped, the length being only 1½ times its width. Both eyes are on the left side, so the fish rests on the sea bottom on its right side. The large mouth is situated to the left of the eyes, the teeth and jaws are equal on both sides. The dorsal fin starts at the snout and, like the anal fin, does not join with the tail fin. The pelvic fins are broad at the base, that on the eyed side being slightly longer than that on the blind side. The turbot is scaleless but its upper side is covered with small, scattered bony knobs or tubercles. These are much smaller and closer together on the head. The colour varies according to that of the seabed on which it is lying, ranging from a dull grey when on mud or muddy sand to a pale yellow on sand. The underside is white but may bear patches of colour. A few turbot are ambicoloured—coloured on both sides.

The brill is closely related to the turbot and is similar in form and habits but it is relatively unimportant as a food fish. The Black Sea turbot is another related form with much larger tubercles on both the lower and upper surfaces.

The turbot ranges from the Mediterranean to the North Sea as far north as Bergen on the Norwegian coast, sometimes wandering north of the Arctic Circle as far as Lofoten Islands. It is found all round the coasts of the British Isles but is rarely caught as far north as the Orkneys and Shetlands.

Rippling sprinter

The turbot lives in shallow water, rarely being caught in depths of more than 250 ft. Locally it is sometimes found so close to the shore that it can be fished off the beach at low water, but it has not been known to enter estuaries. It normally lies on shell gravel or gravel bottoms but may also be found on sand or mud. Like all flatfishes the turbot swims by rippling undulations of the whole body but each spurt does not carry it very far.

A wide diet

The food of turbot is mainly other fish such as sand eels, sprats, pilchards and members of the cod family. Soles, dabs, dragonets, sea bream and boarfish, a relative of the John Dory, are sometimes taken; invertebrates such as bivalve molluscs and worms have been recorded, but rarely. The larvae of the turbot feed on animal plankton, including the larvae of barnacles and molluscs.

One of the most prolific seafish

In the North and Irish Seas spawning takes place from April to August, in the western Channel and off the Welsh coast from May to September. The turbot is one of the most prolific of seafishes, the female laying 5–10 million eggs, each $\frac{1}{25}$ in. diameter, over gravelly ground in shallow water. Turbot eggs and larvae are pelagic, floating near the surface of the sea. The egg has a pale yellow oil droplet in it that gives buoyancy. After 7–9 days the eggs hatch. At first the fry are very small, $\frac{1}{10}$ in. long, and helpless. They then have a normal shape with an eye on each side of the head. They also have a distinct airbladder which they do not lose until they have changed into little flatfishes. During this change the right eye migrates to the left side of the head to a position next to the left eye. The left side of the body becomes pigmented and the right side becomes white. The change is slow and does not begin until the young turbot is ½ in. long and is sometimes not completed until it is 1 in. long, and 4–6 months old. During this time the baby turbots are widely spread. They do not assume a bottom-living life until after their metamorphosis is complete.

Turbot grow fairly rapidly, the females faster than the males. At 3 years old the males are about 12½ in. long and the females 14¼ in. and at 5 years old the males are 16½ in. long and the females 17½ in. The maximum age recorded is about 15 years, when the average length of males is 21 in. and the females 27 in.

Hazardous beginnings

As the eggs and larvae float near the surface of the sea they are subject to many hazards. They are at the mercy of wind and current and may be carried into waters where they cannot survive, or they may be snapped up by a wide variety of fishes. Changes of temperature may kill them or they may be cast up on the shore to perish. Out of each brood of 10 million eggs, very few turbot reach adulthood. Once fully grown the fish's ability to assume the colour of the sea bottom where it is resting is an effective camouflage concealing it from its enemies.

Ancient fishery

Its fine flavour makes the turbot an important food fish in both the Mediterranean and northern European waters. The chief fishery is in the central area of the North Sea where 88% of the northern European catch is obtained. Fishing is now usually by trawl although some are taken by long lines or even caught in seine nets off the beach in some localities. The turbot is also a favourite fish of anglers; the record fish taken on rod and line in British waters weighed 29 lb. Fishing for turbot with long lines has been going on for centuries in the North Sea. An 18th century account tells how Yorkshire fishermen went out in 20ft boats manned by three men who each had three lines furnished with 280 hooks set 6 ft 2 in. apart. Once on the fishing ground the nine lines were joined, making one long line nearly three miles long and carrying over 2 500 baited hooks.

class	**Pisces**
order	**Pleuronectiformes**
family	**Bothidae**
genus & species	***Scophthalmus maeoticus*** *Black Sea turbot* **S. maximus** *turbot* **S. rhombus** *brill*

2441

Turkey

The wild turkey, a native of America, was domesticated by the Aztecs long before Columbus crossed the Atlantic. The domesticated turkey was brought to Europe and later taken back to what is now the United States.

The male wild turkey is 4 ft from beak tip to the end of the tail and usually weighs about 17½ lb, although 22 lb has been recorded. The females weigh only half this. The plumage is mainly metallic green, bronze and copper with white or pale buff in the wings and upper tail coverts. The male, sometimes the female also, has a tuft of bristles near the base of the neck. The reddish legs and feet are strong, and there is a spur, as in other gamebirds. The head and neck are bare and are decorated with a warty bluish skin, a red throat wattle and a spur-like fleshy caruncle near the base of the beak.

There are two kinds of wild turkey: **Meleagris gallopavo**, known simply as the turkey and **Agriocharis ocellata**, the ocellated turkey. There are five races or subspecies of the first, found only from Pennsylvania southwards. **M. gallopavo silvestris** formerly ranged from Canada to Florida. This was the one the Pilgrim Fathers ate, so establishing turkey as the traditional dish at Thanksgiving, the demand today being met by the fifth subspecies later re-imported from Europe. In southern Florida lives **M. g. osceola**. The third subspecies **M. g. merriami** lives in the foothills of the Rockies. The fourth is the Rio Grande turkey **M. g. intermedia**. The fifth, **M. g. gallopavo**, from which present-day turkeys are descended, is native to the highlands of Mexico, and is the one domesticated by the Aztecs.

▽ *The ugly yet arresting head of an ocellated turkey, covered by a typical warty bluish skin.*

▷ *Despite the apparent arrogance of the wild turkey it is shy and will quickly run if disturbed.*

Wolfgang Lummer

Shyness not enough

Turkeys live in open mixed woodlands, moving over the ground in small flocks by day and roosting in the trees by night. They can fly strongly but seldom stay airborne for more than a quarter of a mile—the longest flight recorded was a mile. They are very shy and quickly disappear into the undergrowth on being disturbed. That has not saved them, however. They are vulnerable to the shotgun when roosting silhouetted against a moonlit sky, as well as providing sport by day. Perhaps the main cause of the decline in their numbers, which is especially marked in some subspecies such as *silvestris*, has been the destruction of their habitat. The felling of trees and the opening up of the land has everywhere diminished the range of wild turkeys, by robbing the birds of cover as well as their natural food.

Food of the woods

Like the pheasant, to which they are nearly related, turkeys eat a wide variety of plant and animal foods. Insects, especially grasshoppers, are eaten in large numbers as well as seeds and berries, such as dewberries, blackberries and strawberries growing in the glades and grasslands of the open forests. They also rely a good deal on acorns and mast from the trees and, until they were felled, on the fruits from chestnuts. Turkeys usually drink twice a day.

Gobblers and their harems

The male turkey, or gobbler, is polygamous. After mating, the females go their own ways to make a nest in a depression in the ground under low vegetation, and in thickets. Each lays one egg a day, to a total of 8–15. It is large and lightly spotted with reddish-brown. Incubation begins when the clutch is complete and lasts 28 days. The eggs usually hatch in the afternoon, the chicks being led away by the hen, with no help from the male. For the first two weeks the chicks roost on the ground. Then they fly at night to a low branch where they settle themselves either side of the mother, who curves her wings over them.

Half the chicks lost

Infancy is the most dangerous stage of a turkey's life. Opossums, raccoons, and others raid the nests, and after hatching there are further losses, especially when the chicks roost on the ground. By September half the chicks have been killed.

The ocellated turkey

The ocellated turkey, which takes its name from the 'eyes' or ocelli on its tail, has fared little better than its more familiar relative, having been wiped out in much of its former range. It is smaller, a male weighing 11 lb, a female just over half this, and more colourful than the North American species. It lacks the 'beard' of bristles on the upper breast and its neck is blue with red caruncles on the head. Its breeding habits are much the same except that the males and females form mixed flocks outside the breeding season, whereas in the common turkey they separate. Ocellated turkeys also fly more freely when danger threatens, instead of relying on their legs as the common turkey does.

Why 'turkey'?

The earliest record we have for the domesticated turkey in Europe tells us that Pedro Nino brought some to Spain in 1500, having bought them in Venezuela for four glass beads each. The turkey is known to have reached England by 1524, and by 1558 at least it was becoming popular at banquets. In Spain the new bird was often referred to as the Indian fowl, an allusion which is repeated in the French *dindon*, formed from *d'Inde*. The origin of the name turkey is less obvious. One view is that it is from the bird's call *turk-turk-turk*. A more likely explanation is that in the 16th century merchants trading along the seaboards of the Mediterranean and eastern Atlantic were known as Turks. They probably included the birds in their merchandise and these then became known as turkey fowls.

The domesticated breeds today range from the Norfolk, known in the United States as the black, through the bronze to several breeds of white, including the small white. Whereas formerly size in a turkey was desirable, with the small ovens today the small white is gaining popularity.

class	**Aves**
order	**Galliformes**
family	**Meleagrididae**
genera & species	***Agriocharis ocellata*** ocellated *** Meleagris gallopavo***

▷ Distribution of the wild turkey in the New World and dates of its arrival as a domestic breed in different parts of Europe. Ancestors of present-day domestic turkeys were drawn from the **Meleagris** population.

▽ A 'gobbling' gathering. During the day, small flocks of wild turkeys spend their time roaming over the ground, searching for seeds and insects —a large part of their diet. At night they roost in trees, making them particularly vulnerable to hunters as they are silhouetted against the sky.

▽▷ Puffed up with importance; a 51lb male domesticated turkey, one of the many breeds of the wild turkey, dwarfs a small plump hen.

▽▽ Polygamous domesticated male turkey mates with one of his harem. Turkey rearing is an important and successful part of the poultry industry today, table birds being available for most festive seasons.

Pilgrim Fathers

Spanish Explorers

1524
1560
1518
1500
1556

Turkey

Wild *(Meleagris gallopavo)*

Ocellated *(Agriocharis ocellata)*

Joe Munroe: Photo Res.

Heather Angel

Turkey vulture

The turkey vulture is one of the 'New World vultures', a family of birds of prey very similar in habits and appearance to the true vultures of the Old World. The family includes the two condors (p 510), the yellow-headed vulture **Cathartes burrovianus,** the greater yellow-headed vulture **C. melambrotus,** the black vulture **Coragyps atratus,** and the king vulture

Sarcorhamphus papa. The turkey vulture, also known as the buzzard, is about 29 in. long, weighs about 3 lb and has a 6ft wingspan. The plumage is blackish-brown with a greenish gloss on the body. The head is naked and red, or brownish in young birds. In flight the turkey vulture is distinguished by its long wings and red head.

Turkey vultures range from southern Canada to Tierra del Fuego, including the West Indies and the Falkland Islands.

Grounded by weather

The turkey vulture's distinctive outline in flight is a common and unwelcome sight in many parts of its range, where tales of its killing livestock and spreading disease are widespread. It is found in many types of country, from forests to deserts and the high plateaux of the Andes. In most regions, including the northern and southern parts of its range, the turkey vulture does not migrate, but the Andean population moves to lower levels and turkey vultures in the dry areas of the western United States fly south in winter.

The turkey vulture is an excellent flier, gliding for long distances without a beat of its large wings, or soaring in thermals. It has been calculated that they travel at 40 mph when on migration, following the lie of the land. Turkey vultures roost in trees, sometimes in groups that crouch on their perches like chickens. They leave the roost only when the ground has warmed and there are rising air currents to help them take off. When it rains they may remain perched all day.

The riper the better

As with their relatives of both Old and New Worlds, the food of turkey vultures is mainly carrion, which may be freshly dead or in very advanced stages of decomposition. Compared with other vultures the turkey vulture has a small bill, so it prefers rotten carcases or those already opened.

▽ *Turkey vultures investigate a sandy beach. In the Peruvian guano islands they are considered pests, as they take the eggs and young of seabirds.*

Wolfgang Lummer

△ *Grotesque monarch: with earflaps, warts and wattles, the king vulture is the most distinguished of the New World vultures. It lives in the forested areas of Central and South America, and can sometimes be seen in groups of 25 or more, flying with all the grace of an albatross. The protuberances on the beak may have a sensory function.*

Follow that smell

For over a century there has been controversy about the way in which turkey vultures, and other birds of prey, have been able to spot prey or carrion from great distances. Many experiments have been made to show that turkey vultures have a very limited sense of smell and find their food by sight. Audubon, for instance, covered a carcase with canvas and found that they were not attracted to it but they would come to a canvas with a picture of a dissected sheep on it. A Mr Bachman also covered a putrid carcase with canvas, and then, by scattering meat on it, attracted turkey vultures onto it. They ate the meat but did not detect the decaying meat only a few inches from their nostrils.

Despite the apparent proof of these experiments a number of instances have been recorded of turkey vultures gathering at hidden carcases. The turkey vulture also has relatively large centres of smell in the brain and recent experiments have now proved that turkey vultures find their food at least partly by smell. Furthermore, maintenance engineers recognise that turkey vultures sometimes gather over leaks in gas pipes, where they are apparently attracted by the nasty smell.

The animals killed by motor traffic now provide an abundant source of food. They also catch small live animals, such as mice, and they occasionally take eggs and nestlings of herons and of seabirds on the Peruvian guano islands. Other foods include rotten pumpkins and the fruit of oil palms.

A circle dance

Small groups of turkey vultures have been seen to perform a strange dance during the early part of the breeding season. About six birds gather in a clearing and hop after each other with wings outstretched. One bird hops after a second, who chases a third and so on until they are moving in a circle. This dance apparently precedes mating. Two white eggs are laid on the floor of a cave, in a cranny, in a hollow tree or on the ground in a thicket. Both parents incubate the eggs, which hatch in 38–41 days. The young are able to fly when about 11 weeks old.

Unjustified persecution

Turkey vultures' great enemy is man, either through deliberate hunting or by accident. Ironically, they are hit by cars while feeding on animal carcases from previous collisions. The reason for shooting turkey vultures is that they attack the nests of guano-producing seabirds or kill young livestock. Their predations have no significant effect on the former and instances of the latter must be most unusual as the turkey vulture is too small and its bill too weak to harm a large living animal unless it is very weak or trapped. Another reason for killing turkey vultures, especially in the United States, is that they can spread diseases such as anthrax, which they pick up on their feet and heads from carcases. They are, however, unlikely to transfer the germs to living animals. It is of interest that turkey vultures are immune to the deadly botulinus toxin which must be a hazard to most carrion eaters.

class	**Aves**
order	**Falconiformes**
family	**Cathartidae**
genus & species	***Cathartes aura*** *turkey vulture*

▽ *Full stretch: a turkey vulture exposes the full 6 feet of its wingspan. It is, however, small compared with its relatives. With wings spread like this the vulture prevents over-heating by exposing a massive surface area to any cooling breezes.*

Ron Austing

Turnstone

Turnstones are small waders that turn stones over when searching for food. They are about 9 in. long, a little larger than ringed plovers. With the surfbird, the two species of turnstones form a subfamily usually classed with the sandpipers (p 2021) but sometimes with the plovers (p 1793). The bill is fairly short and stout; the legs are also rather short. The turnstone, known in North America as the ruddy turnstone, has a very distinctive summer plumage. The upperparts are 'tortoiseshell' with rusty red on the back. The head, neck and underparts are white but there is a very conspicuous pattern of black lines over the head and across the breast. The legs are orange. In winter the head, breast and back become dark brown, except for the throat, which remains white. The pattern of the summer plumage breaks up the outline of the turnstone and makes it extremely difficult to see when it is feeding among the pebbles on a beach. In flight, however, the piebald pattern shows up very well. The ruddy turnstone is found around the globe in Arctic regions, around the coasts of Alaska, northern Canada, Greenland, Scandinavia and Siberia. At one time it nested on the northern coast of Germany but it has now disappeared, probably because of the warmer weather during this century.

The black turnstone breeds only in Alaska, where it nests inland. Its plumage is more uniform than that of the ruddy turnstone. It lacks the rusty colour on the back, and the head and breast are mainly black with white speckles on the side of the breast. These disappear in winter. The surfbird also breeds only in Alaska, nesting in mountains above the tree line. It is mottled black and white over most of the body, becoming uniformly darker in winter.

Speedy migration

Turnstones migrate long distances between their breeding and wintering grounds. The ruddy turnstone travels south to the Cape Province of South Africa, Chile and even Australia and New Zealand. Some, presumably juveniles, stay there while the remainder fly north to breed. The black turnstone and the surfbird spread down the Pacific coast of America. One turnstone gave a good indication of the speed at which birds migrate. It was ringed in Germany at 11 am one day, and was recovered on the northwest coast of France at 12 am the following day, having travelled just over 500 miles at an average of 38 mph.

While on migration turnstones fly in large flocks at a considerable height but when not travelling they fly low and in small parties, circling over the sea and returning quickly to the shore when disturbed. Turnstones often associate with other waders and fight them when competing for food.

Heinz Schrempp

Turnstones by name and nature

When feeding along the shore turnstones eat small animals such as winkles, worms and crustaceans, as well as the eggs of other birds and carrion. Inland on the breeding grounds they feed mainly on insects and their larvae, such as beetles and caterpillars. Their name is derived from the way they flick over stones, clods of earth or seaweed, to expose the small animals underneath. They bend their legs, then insert the slightly upcurved bill under the object and flick it over, sometimes pushing with the breast if it gets stuck halfway. Stones up to ½ lb can be shifted in this way, flat ones being more difficult to move than round ones. It sometimes appears as though turnstones co-operate with each other to turn heavy stones but they are just as likely to work against each other as to lever in the same direction. Sandhoppers are found by flicking over seaweed, while small molluscs and worms are exposed by digging into the sand. The stone-turning habit, however, is not so common as the name suggests as turnstones spend much of their time feeding along the water's edge like perfectly normal waders.

Inland nest sites

Ruddy turnstones usually nest near the shore but sometimes they choose islands some distance up rivers. The black turnstone and the surfbird regularly nest inland, the former on the banks of pools in the tundra and the latter in rocky outcrops in mountainous regions. It has been said that the breeding grounds of the surfbird are identical to those of mountain sheep.

The nest is a scantily lined scrape in the ground in which four eggs are laid. Both parents incubate the eggs and feed the chicks. Turnstones defend their broods vigorously, harassing any enemies, especially skuas and Arctic foxes.

△ *Although turnstones feed along the water's edge like other waders, their favourite haunt is around stones and pebbles on the shore — as shown by this ruddy turnstone. The stones are turned and flicked over with the strong bill. They also eat birds' eggs and in Alaska they have been seen feeding on seal carcases.*

Grisly diet

Turning over stones and clods is not the only unusual feeding habit of turnstones. Alexander Wetmore describes how migrating turnstones feed on terns' eggs on Laysan Island. Whenever the terns were disturbed and flew off their nests, parties of turnstones would alight and peck holes in the eggs. They also tried to attack the eggs of boobies and frigate birds but these were too tough. Two turnstones even dragged an egg from under a sitting tern and ate it there and then. Another surprising habit is that of carrion-eating. In Alaska turnstones seem to feed on the carcases of slaughtered fur seals, although it may be merely that they are feeding on the maggots in them. However, in *British Birds* for 1966 AJ Mercer records seeing turnstones definitely feeding on the flesh of a human corpse washed up on the beach. Turnstones also exploit humans by feeding on edible refuse such as potato peelings.

class	**Aves**
order	**Charadriiformes**
family	**Scolopacidae**
genera & species	***Aphriza virgata*** *surfbird*
	Arenaria interpres *ruddy turnstone*
	A. melanocephala *black turnstone*

Turtle dove

The turtle dove is one of the smaller members of the pigeon family, and one of the least harmful to agriculture. It is of special interest because its habits, especially its migrations, are particularly closely linked with its food supply.

It is about 10 in. long, red-brown on the upper parts, grey on the head, the throat and breast being vinous shading to white on the underparts. The centres of the wing feathers are black. The eye is deep red. The bill is relatively weak. There are patches of black and white feathers on the sides of the neck, used in display. The tail has long graduated black feathers, all white-tipped, except the central one.

The turtle dove winters in tropical Africa but migrates north to breed in north Africa, southwest Asia, and Europe, as far north as Norway, Sweden and Finland.

A peaceful chorus

In contrast to the wood pigeon, with which it shares much the same range in summer, the turtle dove frequents open woodlands, parkland and shrubberies. It is seldom found on buildings, and prefers to perch on low or medium sized trees and bushes near cultivated ground. There are few more restful or pleasant sounds than the call of the turtle dove in the stillness following the dawn chorus. The Latin name for the dove was *turtur*, from its call. Originally called dove' in Old English, it later became the turtur dove and finally turtle dove. In *The Song of Solomon* there is mention of the belief that the cooing of the turtle dove heralded the approaching spring.

Feeds on weed seeds

The summer diet of turtle doves has been very fully analysed, particularly by RK Murton. From the end of April or the beginning of May, when the doves reach their summer grounds, to the end of June, they feed mainly in hayfields. From July to September they feed mainly among cereal and other crops. Their food is 95% seeds of weeds, with about 3% animal food, mainly small snails. The weed seeds include those of grasses but are predominantly the fruits of fumitory *Fumaria* spp. A recent report shows that the seeds of millet, a commercial crop in the USSR, are particularly suitable for the turtle dove, so there the bird is a potential pest especially in spring when the ground is newly sown. Nevertheless, the report concludes: 'as they mainly pick up seeds that are badly embedded in the earth or lying on the surface, and whose germination is improbable, the harm that the doves cause should be reckoned as inconsiderable'.

Elsewhere the distribution of turtle doves is closely linked with that of the fumitory. In Britain, for example, the fumitory, a weed of cultivated ground, is common over much of England, rarer in Wales and absent from most of Scotland, and the distribution of the turtle dove follows these limits.

▷ *The turtle dove is a summer visitor over most of Europe and some parts of North Africa and Asia.*
◁ *On its nest among the brambles, a parent turtle dove feeds its hungry family. Their food is 'pigeon's milk' regurgitated from the crop of the adult bird. The young insert their bills into that of the parent and stimulate production of this nutritious, curdlike liquid. A pair of doves will raise 2 or 3 broods a season in this way, sharing the incubation and feeding.*

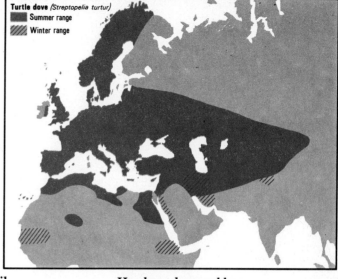

Turtle dove *(Streptopelia turtur)*
■ Summer range
▨ Winter range

Early families in peril

The territorial display of the turtle dove consists of launching out from a perch, then climbing steeply before gliding down and circling back to the perch again. During courtship the male displays to the female by puffing out his chest and bobbing up and down in front of her with lowered bill.

The nest is a frail platform of thin twigs, sometimes lined with roots, hair or plant stems. Two white, oval or elliptical eggs are laid, and usually each pair of doves has 2 or 3 clutches in a season. The parents share the incubation for 14 days and feed the nestlings on 'pigeon's milk', a secretion from their crop, for 18 days. Egg-laying reaches its peak in the second half of May and early June then declines during July, to end abruptly in September. The supply of seeds improves as the summer wears on and there is a higher rate of survival among young born in the second half of the breeding season. This is because the parents need to spend less time looking for food so the losses from nest-robbing predators are fewer. Even so, there are heavy losses over the season as a whole. Nest-robbers take 34% of the eggs, only 47% hatch and only 39% produce fledged young. The nest robbers are other birds, the magpie and the jay being very active thieves, especially during the early part of the breeding season.

Learning the hard way

Towards the end of August there is a decline in the breeding impulse and the parents tend to desert their eggs and young. Even if they continue to feed the nestlings their waning parental instinct means the young may not get sufficient food to lay in the stores of fat needed on migration. This leads to further deaths on migration, already hazardous for young doves. It has been found that on the journey south in September through western Europe the young and inexperienced birds take a more westerly route than the old birds, flying down the coast of Portugal. There is danger on this route of their being blown out to sea by the prevalent easterly winds. Moreover, young birds tend to migrate under unfavourable weather conditions, so instead of being able to fly high they must come down, within range of the shotgun.

Hawks and egg-robbers

The predators of turtle doves are mainly hawks, such as sparrowhawks, and the nest robbers including the magpie and jay. The latter are always on the lookout for unguarded nests so their impact is greatest during the early part of the season, when food is less plentiful and the parents must absent themselves more from the nest. From all causes, there is a 50% mortality among adult turtle doves made good each year by surviving young ones.

Unusual moult

In summer, turtle doves work to a tight schedule as breeding continues late into the year, leaving little time before migration to go through a moult. This may be because they do not have sufficient energy to spare for this exacting process without depriving the body of fat reserves needed for the migration journey. As a result they start the moult and then migrate with an arrested moult, which is not completed before they reach their winter quarters.

Standing weeds needed

The question then arises why, in the face of normal hazards and other dangers, turtle doves should migrate at all. Climate seems not to be the determining factor since turtle doves can be kept in outdoor aviaries throughout the winter in England, provided they are well fed. In the wild there should be no shortage of weed seeds on the ground. The need to migrate may well be linked with the pattern of the turtle dove's feeding behaviour. They take mainly the seeds from standing vegetation. The fumitory, and other wild plants supplying their food, die down at the end of summer, and turtle doves have little skill in taking seeds from the ground.

class	**Aves**
order	**Columbiformes**
family	**Columbidae**
genus & species	***Streptopelia turtur***

Tyrant-flycatcher

The tyrant-flycatchers are a vast group of birds, with over 300 species including birds with the common names of kingbird, kiskadee, phoebe and pewee. They are similar but not related to the true flycatchers (p 791). Confined to the New World, they have taken up many ways of life and are so widely varied in appearance that generalisation is nearly impossible. Many have a short crest and a bright patch of colour on the crown. The wings may be rounded or pointed and the bills also vary greatly. Tyrant-flycatchers range in length from 3 to 9 in.

Some of the tyrant-flycatchers are brightly coloured. The vermilion flycatcher has a red head and underparts with a brown back. The many-coloured tyrant has feathers of black, blue, green, orange, scarlet and white. The 15in. scissor-tailed flycatcher has a black and white forked tail making up over half its total length and the northern royal flycatcher has a fan-shaped crest of orange and violet. Most tyrant-flycatchers are, however, rather inconspicuously coloured with shades of brown and grey.

Tyrant-flycatchers range from the treeline in Canada to the tip of South America, including the Galapagos and Falkland Islands, but most are found in the tropics.

Variety of lives

The habitats of tyrant-flycatchers are extremely varied and this is correlated with their variability in body form. Long-winged species are migratory, while those with short rounded wings live in forests, and in open country there are tyrant-flycatchers with strong legs, like pipits. Tyrant-flycatchers range from sea-level to 12 000 ft in the Andes and live in grassland, dense forests and swamps. Not surprisingly their feeding and nesting habits are also very varied. Their songs are poor and not particularly pleasant; the kiskadees and pewees are named after their calls.

Many feeding habits

In their feeding the tyrant-flycatchers show many of the habits of familiar Old World flycatchers. Most feed on insects but their diet is often supplemented with fruit and larger animals. Like the Old World flycatchers, they wait on a favoured perch and fly out to catch passing insects with an audible snap of the bill. Their ability to catch flying insects is assisted by the rictal bristles around the base of the bill which act as a net. Rictal bristles are best developed in the 'fly-catching' species and are much reduced in those that catch larger prey or eat fruit. Instead of catching flying insects, some tyrant-flycatchers, such as the grey pepoaza, pounce on terrestrial insects as shrikes do, and those with strong legs chase them on the ground or fly up to snap a low-flying insect, like wheatears. Others hunt insects among foliage like warblers.

The larger species, such as the boat-billed flycatcher, feed on small birds, lizards, frogs and mice, battering their victims before tearing them apart. The black phoebe catches fish, and to complete this example of contrasts, the fire-crowned tyrant searches the backs of cattle for insects and ticks, like an oxpecker.

Snakeskin decorations

Tyrant-flycatchers are almost as varied in their nesting habits as in their feeding habits. The nests may be open cups or domed nests, on the ground or in the fork of a tree, camouflaged or conspicuous. Some take over the holes of woodpeckers, others usurp the mud nests of oven birds and a few nest near wasps, sheltering under the protection of these aggressive neighbours. The majority of species, however, build cup-shaped nests of grass and twigs in the branches of trees. Many tropical species build purse-like domed nests with tubular entrances.

The great-crested flycatcher, a hole-nester using woodpecker holes, bird-boxes and so on, sometimes decorates its nest with cast-off snakeskins. It is often said that this habit is a protective device to scare away predators. About 15 other species of birds are known to do this, including the riflebird and a bird of paradise, but it is difficult to see that predators would be scared by a snakeskin if the nest builder was not scared to pick it up in the first place. Presumably the snakeskins are merely one of the many odd objects that have been found in birds' nests merely because they are convenient materials.

The eggs vary from pure white to white with spots and streaks and the clutch number varies from two in the tropics to four in higher latitudes. Both parents build the nest but only the female incubates. The incubation and fledging periods also vary. They are usually 14–18 and 13–14 days respectively, but incubation may last 19–23 days and the fledging period may be 21–25 days. Both parents feed the young and there may be two or more broods a year, especially in the tropics.

Little tyrants

The kingbirds of the genus *Tyrannus* are aptly named because of the way they harass other birds that come into their territories. The eastern kingbird of North America was known as the 'Little Chief' from the way it attacked humans who ventured near its nest and did not hesitate to attack crows or hawks much larger than itself. Even if the intruders show no interest in the kingbird and its brood they are pursued until well away from the nest. Kingbirds are not the only aggressive flycatchers. RE Mumford describes how the acadian flycatcher attacks cowbirds, which may try to lay their eggs in its nest, squirrels, chipmunks and even inoffensive nuthatches.

◁ *Vermilion flycatcher* **Pyrocephalus rubinus**.

class	Aves
order	Passeriformes
family	Tyrannidae
genera & species	*Empidonax virescens* acadian *Machetornis rixosa* fire-crowned *Megarhynchus pitangua* boat-billed *Muscivora forficata* scissor-tailed *Myiarchus crinitus* great-crested *Onychorhynchus mexicanus* northern royal *Pyrocephalus rubinus* vermilion *Sayornis nigricans* black phoebe *Tachuris rubrigastra* many-coloured *Tyrannus tyrannus* eastern kingbird *Xolmis cinerea* grey pepoaza others

Uakari

Uakari

The uakari (pronounced wakari) is a little-known monkey of South America, closely related to the saki (p 2010) but differing from it in a number of features, especially the short tail. It is the only South American monkey whose tail is actually shorter than the head and body, which measure 16—18 in., the tail being only 6—7 in. The body is covered with shaggy hair, variable in colour, but underneath it the uakari is a skinny, spidery animal. The head is naked, with only very short, sparse hair or none at all. This utter baldness is accentuated by an almost complete lack of fat under the skin, making the face incredibly lean and bony. In the adult male the jaw muscles become big and bulky, and can be seen clearly beneath the bare skin, bulging out on the top of the skull. The bare face pokes out from a mass of shaggy hair which begins behind the ears and on the neck and the back of the head, so the uakari looks rather like a bald monk with a cape.

There are two species of uakari, found around the Amazon on both sides of its upper course. On the north side, between the rivers Branco, and its tributary the Rio Negro, and Japurá, lives the black-headed uakari, which is chestnut-brown in colour with black hands and feet, and a naked black face. To the southwest, on the other side of the Rio Japurá, lives the bald uakari, which differs in its skull characteristics, and has a longer coat and a pink or red face. The face turns pale if the animal is kept from sunlight and becomes bright crimson if it is allowed to live in the full sun. The bald uakari is divided into two very distinct races: the white one, in which the coat is white or silvery, and the red one, with a coat that is red like the face. The first ranges from the Rio Japurá to the Rio Içá. The second extends south from the Içá to about 7° S, its range bounded on the west and east by the rivers Ucayali and Juruá.

Active in the treetops

Uakaris have rarely been observed in the wild. Their superficial thickness of body has led people to suspect they are clumsy and lethargic, but on seeing how thin a shaved uakari really is, it is not at all surprising to learn that they are in fact agile and active. In the wild they have been seen making leaps of 20 ft or so, launching themselves into the air with arms stretched forwards. On the ground they are somewhat ill at ease, walking with the hands partly flexed, and turned out sideways, but in captivity they invent games for themselves, sliding along the cage floor or turning back somersaults. When feeding they are very dexterous. They hold the food in the whole flexed hand, the thumb not being divergent, or between the index and middle fingers, or even

▷ *Sweet dreams for a relaxed bald uakari.*

between the hand and wrist. They have projecting lower incisors like their relatives the sakis, and these are probably used for spearing the fruits which form part of their diet along with buds, leaves and seeds.

Uakaris have been seen both in small troops and in large gatherings of about 100. They may go right up to the treetops but they come down to the lower branches when travelling through the forest.

Breeding is a closed book

It is a pity that these remarkable animals seem neither to have been bred in captivity, nor to have been observed in the wild to any great extent. So nothing is known of their breeding habits. Even the length of the gestation period is unknown, which is the one thing that is usually known about a mammal even when other details of its breeding remain obscure.

Sedation an old trick

The only thing we possess that approaches an adequate record of uakaris in their natural habitat was written over a century ago. Bates, in 1855, wrote that the bald uakari is captured alive by shooting it with arrows and blowpipes. The curare poison always used with these arrows was, however, diluted in order to capture the monkeys alive. The uakari, when shot, would run quite a long way, and it took a really expert hunter to track one and be underneath it when, weak with the poison, it fell from the branches. As soon as the animal fell a pinch of salt would be put into its mouth, which, so the story ran, acted as an antidote to the poison and revived the monkey. Animals caught in this way were kept as pets, often being traded far from their native haunts. They seem to have developed a great devotion to their owners and they were fairly easy to keep, although the initial death rate was high. Nowadays they are not too uncommon in zoos, but have not yet bred there. Some have lived as much as eight years in captivity. Their weird appearance, especially in the case of the bald species, and their off-beat antics, performed in silence, have made them popular zoo inmates from Bates's time to the present day.

Perhaps the most interesting feature in this story of how the South American Indians caught the uakari alive is that the method anticipated modern usage. Today we are familiar with the way animals that are marked for study purposes, or for transport to wildlife parks, are first immobilized with a drug in a dart shot from a crossbow. There is no substantial difference between this and the blow-pipe darts used long ago by the South American Indians.

class	**Mammalia**
order	**Primates**
family	**Cebidae**
genus & species	*Cacajao calvus* bald uakari *C. melanocephalus* black-headed uakari

◁ *'Old monk' of the forest: the bald uakari*

Urania moth

In Greek mythology Uranus was the husband of the Earth goddess and the father of the planet Saturn. The scientist who called a genus of moths **Urania** was almost certainly moved by the thought that he was dealing with a heavenly being living on earth. The name was first given to New World moths but it has been extended to include all the moths of the family Uraniidae. They are almost entirely limited to the tropics. Some are large, conspicuous day-flying moths, brilliantly coloured and bearing 'tails' on the hindwings like those of the swallowtail butterflies (p 2322), which the urania moths greatly resemble in appearance.

The genus **Urania** is centred on tropical America. The South American **U. leilus,** like most of the moths of this genus, is brilliantly coloured iridescent green and blue with a long tail and broad white fringes. It has a slender body and a wingspan of 3 in. The largest and most brilliant member of the family is **Chrysiridia madagascarensis** of Madagascar which has been called the most magnificently coloured of all animals. Its wings are black, banded with metallic green which changes to blue and gold according to the angle of the light and the hindwings have a patch of glowing copper and purple, and long white fringes around their tailed and deeply scalloped margins. As well as being so spectacular this moth is a classic mystery: why is it in Madagascar when its nearest relatives seem to be the South American uranias rather than any African or Asian moths?

In the Indo-Australian region the species of **Nyctalemon** and **Alcides** are similarly 'swallow-tailed' and some are beautifully coloured with bands of pale blue, green and yellow. The common **Nyctalemon patroclus** of India is banded with brown and white and may be seen sitting on trees and buildings with its wings outspread, as if the whole group of moths were spread out in a display cabinet.

Dazzled into ignorance

It seems almost as if the very brilliance of these moths has taken the collectors' minds off their habits and life histories. Except that the caterpillars feed on leaves and the moths fly by day, little more seems to be known. The females tend to lay eggs on shrubs and bushes of the *Euphorbia* type.

The caterpillars are very diverse in shape and appearance. That of *Chrysiridia* has black spatulate spines and in the northern Indian species *Epicopeia polydora* the caterpillar is covered with white cottony filaments. When the caterpillars pupate they spin a loosely woven silken cocoon. Possibly another reason why so little can be said about the life histories of these moths is that study has been concentrated on the colours of their wings.

PH Ward

△ *Upper surface of a pinned specimen of* **Chrysiridia madagascarensis,** *a brilliant urania moth.*
▽ *Magnificent from all aspects: the underside shows similar colouring — an unusual moth feature.*

PH Ward

▽ *Production of iridescent colours in moth and butterfly scales through interference by thin plates. The detail shows sections across the scales; 'urania type' left, 'morpho type' right.*

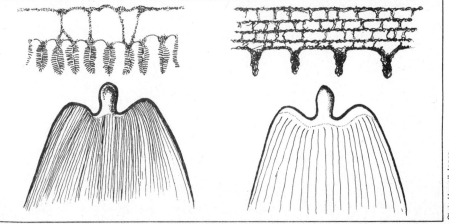

Chris Howell-Jones

2457

Structural coloration

Iridescent or metallic colours that in nature change with the angle of the light are always known as structural colours. This implies that they are not due to pigments which absorb certain wavelengths and reflect others, but to very minute structures which refract and reflect the different wavelengths in different directions. In the wings of butterflies and moths two types of structural coloration are recognised, both depending on 'interference'. This is the physicist's term for colour effects produced when two or more very thin layers or films of a substance are separated by a medium of different refractive index. The 'rainbow colours' shown by a film of oil on water afford an instance of this. The brilliant metallic colours on the wings of some butterflies and moths are produced by interference structures in the scales, and two types are recognised, the 'morpho type' and the 'urania type'. In the former the longitudinal ridges on the scales have extremely minute plates or lamellae projecting from their surfaces (see p 1508). In the urania type, named after the moths under discussion, either the upper or the lower part of the scale is thickened by a number of superimposed layers actually lying in the thickness of the scale and not on ridges standing up out from it. Although the morpho type is named after a butterfly and the urania type after a moth the two types are not characteristic of butterflies and moths respectively, for the glorious bird-wing swallowtail butterflies, for example, have the urania type of coloration.

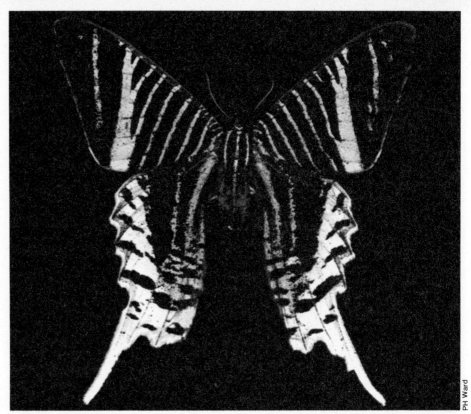

phylum	**Arthropoda**
class	**Insecta**
order	**Lepidoptera**
family	**Uraniidae**

△ *Specimen of* **Urania leilus**, *a day-moving species that flies faster and is more brilliantly coloured than most butterflies.*
▽ *In complete contrast,* **Nyctalemon patroclus** *from New Guinea exhibits the sombre colouring more associated with moths.*

Vampire bat

The vampire bat of fact is totally unlike the vampire of fiction except that it feeds on blood. In one way it is worse than the fictional vampire—it is a carrier of rabies, a disease feared the world over. True vampires, of tropical and subtropical America, feed only on the fresh blood of mammals and birds. Unlike the man-sized vampires of fable, they are only $2\frac{1}{2}$–$3\frac{1}{2}$ in. long with a forearm of 2–$2\frac{1}{2}$ in. The weight of an adult varies in the different species from $\frac{1}{2}$ to $1\frac{1}{4}$ oz. Their fur is various shades of brown. They have no tail. The ears are small and the muzzle short and conical without a true noseleaf. Instead there are naked pads on the snout with U-shaped grooves at the tip, which may be sensory. The upper incisor teeth are large and razor-edged, well adapted for gently opening a small wound to take

blood. The grooved, muscular tongue fits over a V-shaped notch in the lower lip, so forming a tube through which the blood is sucked. The stomach is also adapted for liquid feeding, the forward end being drawn out into a long tube. The saliva contains substances that prevent the blood from clotting.

There are three genera, each with a single species. The common vampire bat, the most numerous and widespread of the three, is distinguished by its pointed ears, longer thumb with a basal pad and its naked interfemoral membrane. It has only 20 teeth. It ranges from northern Mexico southward to central Chile, central Argentina and Uruguay. It is now one of the most common and widespread mammals in eastern Mexico.

The second species, the white-winged vampire, is much less numerous. The edges of its wings and part of the wing membrane are white. It has a peculiar

short thumb about ⅛th as long as the third finger, and has a single pad underneath. It is the only bat known to have 22 permanent teeth. The white-winged vampire is mainly confined to the tropical regions of South America from Venezuela and the Guianas to Peru and Brazil, but it has also been found on Trinidad and in Mexico.

The hairy-legged vampire, smaller than the common species, is not well known. It has shorter, rounded ears, a short thumb without a basal pad and softer fur. Its interfemoral membrane is well-furred. It has 26 teeth and is unique among bats in having a fan-shaped, seven-lobed outer lower incisor tooth which resembles the lower incisor in the order Dermoptera, the gliding lemurs. This species is found in eastern and southern Mexico, Central America, and southwards to Brazil.

▽ Cutting closeup: the bloodstained mouth and shear-like teeth of a common vampire.

AN Warren

Victims attacked while asleep

During the day vampire bats roost in caves, old mines, hollow trees, crevices in rocks and in old buildings. Colonies of the common vampire may number as many as 2 000 but the average is about 100. The sexes roost together and they may share the caves with other species of bats. They are very agile and can walk rapidly on their feet and thumbs either on the ground or up the vertical sides of caves. Shortly after dark the bats leave their roosts with a slow noiseless flight, usually only 3 ft above the ground. The bats attack their victims while they sleep, sometimes alighting near them, crawling up to them, looking rather like large spiders. They make a quick shallow bite with their sharp teeth in a place where there is no hair or feathers. They cut away only a very small piece of skin, making a shallow wound from which they suck the blood without a sound, so the victim does not wake. Unlike other bats they do not cling with their claws but rest lightly on their thumbs and small foot pads, so lightly that even a man is unlikely to be wakened by the visit of a vampire. The common vampire bat in particular can drink such large quantities of blood that it is barely able to fly for some time afterwards.

The common vampire attacks only large mammals such as horses, cattle and occasionally man. Cattle are generally bitten on the neck or leg and a human on the big toe. The white-winged vampire, so far as is known, attacks only birds, biting the neck or ankle, and the hairy-legged vampire appears to prey mainly on birds such as chickens, but it is possible it may also attack some mammals.

In captivity vampire bats have been kept alive on blood defibrinated to prevent clotting. One survived for 13 years in a laboratory in Panama.

Echolocation in vampires

Like all bats, vampires find their way about and detect their prey by echolocation. Since their source of food is large and relatively stationary they do not have the same difficulty in finding their prey as bats that feed on fast-moving insects, or even those that catch fish. Like the fruit-eating bats, which also feed on stationary food, their echolocation is by pulses having only $\frac{1}{1000}$th of the sound energy of those used by bats feeding on insects or fish. It is noteworthy that vampires very seldom attack dogs, presumably because they have more sensitive hearing than larger mammals such as cattle and are able to detect the bat's higher sound frequencies.

Babies left at home

Little or nothing is known of the breeding habits of the white-winged and hairy-legged vampire bats. The common vampire gives birth to a single young after a gestation of 90–120 days. They breed throughout the year and it is possible there is more than one birth a year. The young are not carried about by the mother, as in most other bats, but are left in the roost while she is out foraging.

◁ *Disturbed while sleeping: common vampires prefer retreats of almost complete darkness.*

Desperate measures

The real danger of vampire bats lies not so much in their feeding on the blood of domestic animals and man, although this is bad enough, but in the transmission of disease resulting from the bites and risk of secondary infections. Vampires can transmit rabies which may be fatal in cattle or even in man. They may also transmit the disease to other species of bats and they may die of it themselves. In Mexico alone it is necessary to inoculate thousands of head of cattle each year against the disease. The disease is always fatal to uninoculated cattle.

Various control methods have been tried in the past, including dynamiting the caves where the bats roost and the use of flame-throwers and poison gas. These have been found to be largely ineffective and also highly destructive to other harmless species of bats. The only solution to the problem seems to lie in biological control, including sterilisation, habitat management and the use of selective chemical attractants and repellents. A research centre has now been set up in Mexico City for the ecological study of vampire bats and for research into biological methods of control.

class	**Mammalia**
order	**Chiroptera**
family	**Desmodontidae**
genera & species	***Desmodus rotundus*** *common vampire bat* ***Diaemus youngi*** *white-winged vampire bat* ***Diphylla ecaudata*** *hairy-legged vampire bat*

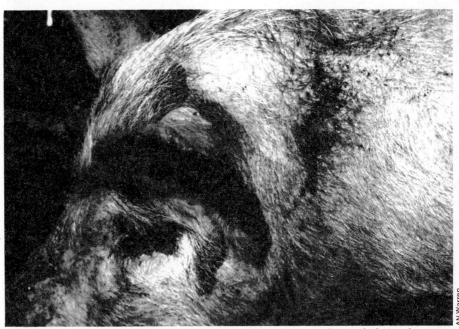

AN Warren

△ *Fresh bites on a pig's neck are grisly evidence of a common vampire's feeding methods. It only feeds on large animals, and because horses and cattle provide such a large supply of easily accessible blood, stockrearing in many tropical areas has proved uneconomical.* ▽ *The culprit on all fours.*

Bruce Hayward

Vanessa

The vanessas include some of the most colourful butterflies in the northern hemisphere, and some of these have a worldwide distribution. The name is from the tribe Vanessidi, a 'tribe' being a taxonomic division of lesser value than a family, the family in this instance being the Nymphalidae. Vanessas have the front pair of legs reduced in size, only the rear two pairs being used for walking. They are fairly large butterflies, with a powerful flight. Most of the species resident in northern Europe pass the winter hibernating as butterflies, others are continuously brooded in the subtropics and migrate northwards in summer. Their caterpillars bear an armature of branched spines and the pupae, or chrysalises, which are suspended by the tail, are ornamented with shining metallic spots. It was the ornamentation of these pupae which led the early butterfly collectors to call themselves 'aurelians', from the Latin **aureus***, golden. 'Chrysalis' has a similar derivation from the Greek* **chrysos** *also meaning golden.*

Seven of the dozen European species are found in Britain and some of these occur in America as well. Eight vanessas are especially interesting in their habits, distribution or life history and the best way to deal with them is to describe each one separately.

Peacock

This beautiful butterfly ranges from Britain eastwards to Japan. It is resident in Britain and spends the winter hibernating in dark sheltered places, often in attics and outhouses. It is quite easy to breed peacock butterflies, by keeping them in a cage in a cool, dark room for the winter. They can then be 'tamed' before releasing them in the spring, so they will remain in the garden and will come to be fed on sugar-water. They have only one generation a year, and the habit of hibernation results in the butterfly having an unusually long life in the winged state. A peacock butterfly in captivity lived for 11 months. Its food plant is nettles.

Red Admiral

The red admiral has a very wide distribution, all over the temperate northern hemisphere and along the Andes nearly to the Equator. Its food plant is nettles.

It is one of the most familiar butterflies in Britain, but it is in fact only a migrant summer visitor, not a resident species. Every year red admirals fly north from the Mediterranean region in the early summer and lay their eggs. There is some evidence that these red admirals fly south again, but nothing is known of the proportion that reach their parents' home in southern Europe.

Camberwell Beauty

This butterfly is known as the mourning cloak in North America. It is, like the red admiral, distributed all over the northern hemisphere, and it also goes down the Andes, in South America. In spite of its wide distribution it is a great rarity in Britain. It appears to need the severe continental type of winter to induce proper hibernation. There is some evidence that the few Camberwell beauties seen in Britain are not true migrants, but stowaways on Scandinavian timber ships. Its food plants are willow, poplar and birch.

Hermann Eisenbeiss

PH Ward

Map butterfly

This little vanessid is widespread in France and elsewhere in Europe. Attempts to introduce it to Britain have failed. It is remarkable in being represented by two distinct seasonal forms. Unlike most vanessids it overwinters as a pupa, and the butterflies which hatch in May are chequered tawny and black and look rather like fritillaries. The larvae from the eggs of these spring butterflies feed and grow rapidly, pupate and produce in July a generation of black-and-white butterflies totally unlike their parents. The length of day during the larval stage determines which form the mature butterfly shall assume. By exposing the caterpillars to long or short 'days', using artificial light, successive generations of either form can be bred. Its food plant is entirely nettles.

Yves Lanceau

Small tortoiseshell

This gay little butterfly ranges right across the Eurasian continent to Japan. It is one of the commonest species in Britain and can be seen in gardens throughout most of the spring and summer as it goes through two generations in a year. The butterflies of the second generation hibernate and reappear in spring. Its food plant is nettles.

Large tortoiseshell

Up to the first two decades of this century this butterfly was not uncommon in southern England, but it has suffered a decline and is now by far the rarest of the resident vanessids in Britain. It is still occasionally seen in Essex and Suffolk and is common in central and southern Europe. Its food consists of elm foliage.

Toni Angermayer

◁ *The rich-hued vanessid of European summer—each year the red admiral flies north from the Mediterranean to lay its eggs.*
▽◁ *Peacock butterflies on a spray of* **Buddleia**, *a favourite food plant of adult butterflies.*
△ *Mourning cloak—a vanessid that hibernates as an adult, feeding on the sugar-rich sap from trees when it emerges in early spring.*
△▷ *Bird's eye view of a small tortoiseshell.*
▷ *The most widespread butterfly in the world—the painted lady. In the spring it migrates in vast numbers from North Africa to Europe.*
▽ *The tattered look of the comma provides excellent camouflage when the wings are folded.*

They taste with their toes

As already mentioned, all the nymphalid butterflies (vanessas, fritillaries, emperors and others) are 'quadrupeds', the forelegs being stunted and not used for walking. Those of the males have only two terminal joints and are brush-like. In the females these legs are more slender with four terminal joints and are only sparsely haired. They are used as sense organs, the end joints serving as organs of taste. A red admiral can distinguish, by touching with its forefeet, between pure water and a sugar solution $\frac{1}{200}$ of the strength required to be detected by the human tongue.

Spare the nettles

Farmers and people obsessed with the idea of 'tidiness' wage a relentless war on nettles, spraying them ruthlessly wherever they grow. But nettles should be allowed to grow in places that are not needed for cultivation or pasture. Five of the vanessid butterflies described here depend on nettles for their larval food. If those who aim to exterminate this plant had their way we should see much fewer gaily coloured butterflies in the gardens of Europe.

PH Ward

Hermann Eisenbeiss

Comma butterfly

The recent history in Britain of this very attractive butterfly is in curious contrast to that of the large tortoiseshell. Up to about 1920 it was confined to a small area in South Wales, but about that time it began to spread over southern England and the Midlands and has maintained this wider distribution. Like the other resident British vanessids it hibernates as a butterfly, but remains in the open in woods and hedges, sheltering under leaves instead of seeking shelter in natural hollows or buildings. When its wings are closed the coloration and irregular outline make the butterfly look like a withered leaf. Without this the butterfly would never survive the hunting of winter-hungry birds. It goes through two generations in the summer and the larva feeds on nettles and elm.

Painted Lady

This is known as the thistle butterfly in North America. It has the distinction of being the only butterfly with a world-wide distribution, without the formation of any well defined races or subspecies. The reason for this is that the urge to migrate is so powerful and persistent in this butterfly that its populations are subject to constant mixing, which of course prevents the formation of local races. In Britain and northern Europe the painted lady is a summer migrant of the same type as the red admiral. The main breeding ground of the European painted ladies is North Africa, and travellers there have witnessed the hatching of thousands of pupae among the sand dunes and the start of the butterflies' massed flight towards the Mediterranean. Its food plant is thistles.

phylum	**Arthropoda**
class	**Insecta**
order	**Lepidoptera**
family	**Nymphalidae**
genera & species	***Aglais urticae*** *small tortoiseshell* ***Araschnia levana*** *map butterfly* ***Nymphalis antiopa*** *Camberwell beauty, or mourning cloak* ***N. io*** *peacock butterfly* ***N. polychloros*** *large tortoiseshell* ***Polygonia c-album*** *comma* ***Vanessa atalanta*** *red admiral* ***V. cardui*** *painted lady or thistle butterfly, others*

Vanga

The 12 vangas or vanga-shrikes form a family of birds confined to Madagascar. They are shrike-like in appearance but owing to the isolation of Madagascar they have evolved quite separately, so it is difficult to trace their relationships with other birds. The vangas have been compared with the wood hoopoes, wood swallows and the shrikes, but as the least specialised vangas, like Chabert's vanga, look like the bush-shrikes of the African mainland, it seems most likely that the vangas are derived from bush-shrikes that crossed to Madagascar.

Vangas are 5–12 in. long, usually black above and white below, but some have brighter colours. The blue vanga, for instance, is bright blue on the head, back, wings and tail, with some black on the flight feathers and white underneath. The rufous vanga has a black head, white underparts and a rufous brown back. The red-tailed vanga resembles a finch and is predominantly greyish brown above and white underneath. The face is black with white eye rings and the male has a black crescent on the breast. In some species the sexes are similar but the male Bernier's vanga is all black while the female is mainly rufous. As with other passerine families such as the Hawaiian honeycreepers (p 1093) and Darwin's finches (p 615) which have evolved in the isolation of islands, the greatest variation of form lies in the bill. Some vangas have relatively simple finchlike or shrikelike bills, others have strangely shaped bills, like the helmetbird, which resembles a miniature toucan with its exaggerated blue bill that is deeper than the skull, and the sicklebill, once thought to be a starling, with a long curved bill.

Childish chatter

There are three families of birds found only in Madagascar, the asities or false sunbirds, the mesites (p 1456) and the vangas, and they must be the least known of all bird families. There are very few published records of the habits of the vangas and even these have been compiled incidentally by ornithologists making a general survey of Madagascan birds, so that they are little more than the results of observations made while other birds were being studied.

All vangas live in trees, mostly in the now fast-disappearing forest, but also in scrubland, mangrove swamps and savannah with scattered trees. Most forage together in small parties of about a dozen, sometimes several species flocking together, but the hook-billed vanga is more solitary. They are usually seen in the treetops, where they travel through the foliage with great agility, calling to each other with a variety of whistles and chattering calls. Sicklebills sometimes utter a bedlam of groans, cries and laughs. Their local name is *voronzaza* or 'bird baby' because of their childlike calls.

△ A painting by Keulemans of a male—grasping an insect—and female vanga, **Cyanolanius bicolor**. The sexes do not differ to this extent in all vangas.

Peter J Green

Acrobatic feeders

The food of vangas is, as far as is known, insects and other small animals up to the size of chameleons. Most vangas feed in the foliage or along twigs and branches, picking off small and medium-sized insects or probing for them in crevices. When foraging, some vangas behave remarkably like the familiar tits, agilely flitting among the foliage and hanging upside down to reach awkward places. Some of the larger vangas hunt like shrikes, waiting on a perch then dropping on their prey. The white-headed vanga and the hook-billed vanga, among others, include a large proportion of vertebrate animals such as tree frogs, chameleons and lizards in their diets.

Nesting habits unknown

Virtually nothing is known of the nesting habits of vangas and even the nests of many species have yet to be discovered. The sicklebill, however, has been watched while building its cup-shaped nest of dead twigs about 30 ft up in a tree. The female collected and carried the twigs while the male accompanied her. The clutch consists of 3 or 4 white or green spotted eggs.

Why the variety?

Darwin's finches (p 615) are a classic example of adaptive radiation. A single ancestral finch species apparently reached the Galapagos Islands where, through lack of competition, it evolved into a large number of species, each occupying a certain habitat or having a particular feeding habit. The differences between the many Darwin's finches lie mainly in the shape of the bill which has been adapted for these various feeding habits. It seems that the vangas also provide an example of adaptive radiation, some ancestor having arrived in Madagascar where there was also little competition from other kinds of birds. The vangas have also evolved different shaped bills, as has already been described, but with the present state of knowledge of the family it has not been possible to relate the different vangas to different habitats or feeding habits.

class	**Aves**
order	**Passeriformes**
family	**Vangidae**
genera & species	**Aerocharis prevostii** helmetbird **Calicalicus madagascariensis** red-tailed vanga **Falculea palliata** sicklebill **Leptopterus chabert** Chabert's vanga **L. madagascarinus** blue vanga **L. viridis** white-headed vanga **Oriolia bernieri** Bernier's vanga **Schetba rufa** rufous vanga **Vanga curvirostris** hook-billed vanga

Vapourer moth

The most distinctive feature of the vapourer moths is the great difference between the males and females. The males are active little moths, with a wingspan of just over 1 in. They fly mainly in sunshine, although they are recorded as coming to an artificial light at night. Most of the females, and certainly all those of the European species, are wingless and look like fat six-legged spiders, and they are so inactive that they never leave the cocoons which enclose their pupae. The larvae feed usually on the leaves of various trees and bushes, but that of one European species lives on heather.

The name was first given to the species **Orgyia antiqua** in 1782. A vapourer then was the term for a braggart or a tongue-wagging talker. The male of the vapourer moth is reddish brown and almost the only decoration on its wings is a white eye-spot on the rear of the forewings; there is no white mark at the tip of the wings. There is nothing to boast of in this, so the name may have been suggested by the male moth's fluttering flight.

The vapourer is one of the tussock moths and its common name was later given to related species, such as the scarce vapourer and the heather vapourer. There are other related species in temperate Asia and a closely related North American species is the white-marked tussock moth.

△ Confined for life: the common vapourer female lays her eggs on her cocoon. Her life history is simple – she develops and mates in her cocoon, lays her eggs on it and then dies.

Wind-blown caterpillars

The common vapourer moths hatch from the pupae in late summer. The females remain in their cocoons where the males seek them out, guided by their scent. Even dead and preserved females have been known to attract males into a room with an open window. Having mated the female lays her eggs on the surface of the cocoon and then dies. The young larvae are covered with very long hairs and have the habit, in common with many small caterpillars, of letting themselves down on silken threads when alarmed. They are then easily blown about by the wind, like thistledown, and may travel long distances. This is, in fact, the only means of dispersal they have, apart from the larva's limited powers of crawling, since the female is completely sedentary.

Male and female caterpillars

The grown larvae are prettily coloured, and ornamented with tufts and strands of hair. If a cocoon covered with eggs is found and the larvae are hatched and reared in captivity a curious activity will be seen. About half of them reach maturity and pupate while the rest feed for about ten days longer and grow to a much larger size before spinning their cocoons. Then, on opening one of the earlier cocoons and one of the later their respective pupae will be seen to differ both in size and appearance.

The smaller ones are males and the larger ones females. This is one of the rare instances in which the sex of a caterpillar can be recognised. The males are the first to appear after pupation. The females, however, begin to emerge long before the last of the males, so the time lag is less marked than it was in the pupating stage.

A grisly cradle

The three European species show an interesting sequence in the degree to which the females become inactive. The female common vapourer comes right out of the cocoon and lays her eggs on its outside. The female scarce vapourer lays them between the inner and outer layers of the cocoon, while the female heather vapourer stays right inside the cocoon for mating and dies there as well, her eggs overwintering in her dead, dried-up body. In a South African species *Bracharoa dregei*, closely related to the vapourer moths, the female behaves rather like that of the heather vapourer, but her eggs hatch soon after mating and the larvae make their first meal of their mother's still-living body.

The North American white-marked tussock moth is similar to the European vapourer in appearance and habits. It is sometimes a minor pest of trees and shrubs. In a Japanese vapourer the male is a normal vapourer moth but there are two forms of the female, one fully winged and resembling the male but larger, and one with vestigial wings.

Why no wings?

There are a number of species of moths with wingless females, but in almost all cases they are species in which mature moths emerge in winter. The winter moth, a notorious pest of orchards, is an example. It has been suggested that if the females of such species had wings, winter gales might blow them far away from the place where they lived as larvae, perhaps even out to sea, where they would perish.

No such explanation can be given for the vapourer females, and the reason for their wingless condition remains a mystery. All that can be said is that there is a tendency for the females of all tussock moths to show a reluctance to fly. The female gypsy moth, for example, never flies although she is fully winged, and the larvae of gypsy moths are known to be dispersed by wind like those of the vapourers. It is of interest that the Japanese vapourer has both winged and wingless females.

JD Bradley

G Temple: NHPA

class	**Insecta**
order	**Lepidoptera**
family	**Lymantriidae**
genera & species	***Orgyia antiqua*** *common vapourer* **O. ericae** *heather vapourer* **O. leucostigma** *white-marked tussock* **O. thyellina** *Japanese vapourer* **O. recens** *scarce vapourer others*

△ *Bizarre but beautiful: the caterpillar of the common vapourer moth displays its ornamental tufts and strands of hair. When handling this larva care must be taken as the hairs can cause severe skin irritation.*
◁ *The sluggish female and winged male common vapourer moths on their cocoon. The male's only attributes are the white eye-spots on his wings. They occur practically over the whole of Europe, and also in northeast Asia Minor, Armenia, Siberia and North America.*

Velvet ant

Velvet ants are some of the biggest frauds in the animal kingdom. Although called ants they are, in fact, solitary wasps. Their common name is due to the marked difference between the male and female. The female is wingless and is therefore forced to run about over the ground, looking like a big hairy ant. The male is winged and so attracts little attention among other wasps that fly around.

The bodies of velvet ants are covered with a pile of short velvet-like bristles, often patterned in black, bright orange and scarlet. Even the antennae are covered with these short hairs. The 3 000 species are all much alike in colour, and most of them live in the hotter, drier parts of the world, and especially in America. A few live in temperate latitudes, including Europe, and two live in Britain. All velvet ants are parasitic on the larvae and pupae of other insects, including bees and wasps. There are even velvet ants that parasitize other solitary wasps, the hunting wasps, that themselves prey on other insects. Some of the desert species have a thick covering of long whitish hairs. The smallest velvet ant **Mutilla lilliputiana** is $\frac{1}{8}$ in. long and the largest, **Dasymutilla occidentalis**, of the southeastern United States, is 1 in. or more long and is known as the cow-killer or mule-killer. The so-called large velvet ant of Britain **Mutilla europaea** is only about $\frac{1}{2}$ in. long. In many species the male is nearly twice the size of the female, but in the three for which sizes are given here the females are only slightly smaller than the males.

▽ Wasp parasitzes wasp: a South African velvet ant lanys her eggs in the nest of a mud-dauber wasp; on hatching the larvae will eat the host's eggs. (Approx × 15.)

Well armed and defended

Velvet ants are equipped for entering the nests of bees and other wasps; they are not only armed but armoured. They have unusually thick and hard outer coverings and entomologists report having difficulty in pushing a steel pin through the thorax of a dead velvet ant when adding a specimen to their cabinet. The males are without a sting and can be handled with impunity. The female, however, has a long and formidable sting, although the power of its venom has often been exaggerated. There is no reason to suppose, for example, that it could cause the death of a large quadruped such as a mule or cow. The female can, however, sting the hand painfully, if handled carelessly, and it is presumably lethal to the insects, such as bumble-bees, whose nests the velvet ants parasitize.

Both male and female of the large velvet ant make a squeaking sound by stridulation, using a file-and-scraper type of organ which is situated about halfway along the upper surface of the body.

The female velvet ants are usually encountered running actively on the ground near the nests of the species which they victimise, or they may be found actually in the nests if these are opened up. The males visit flowers and are generally noticed only by entomologists with specialised knowledge.

A rough wedding

In temperate regions males and females appear and mate in spring. Professor HM Lefroy, in describing the mating of tropical species, spoke of the males as powerful insects. When one finds a female he 'seizes the female by the thorax and flies off; on some convenient spot he mates with her, clasping her firmly to him by his forelegs and standing erect on the others . . . in the frequent intervals the male shook the female with a twisting motion as we would shake a bottle whose contents we desired to mix.'

Eaten out of house and home

After mating, the female runs about, probably covering considerable distances, until she finds an established bumble-bees' nest, or the nest of whichever kind of insect she battens upon. Then she enters. She is well equipped to resist any attempts to evict her, and remains in the nest, feeding on the bees' store of honey, and eventually she lays her eggs in the pupal cells or cocoons of the bees, one egg in each cell. The larvae from these eggs feed on the host pupae, then they themselves pupate, coming out later as adult wasps. In temperate latitudes they pass the winter as pupae in the bees' nest, which is abandoned by the bees at the end of the summer.

There is a record of a bumble-bees' nest dug out of the ground containing 76 velvet ants and only two bumble-bees. This is probably an abnormally high number but it illustrates how effective the female velvet ant must be in coping with the efforts of the female bumble-bee, the rightful owner of the nest, to drive her out.

A coat to keep cool

The female 'velvet ant' wasp, by her appearance, tricked the ordinary person into giving her the misleading common name. The behaviour of both the females and the males made it difficult for scientists to study them. As a result not a great deal is known about them, and nobody seems to have carried out precise experiments to test why they should have such unusually hairy bodies. We can only guess that it serves as an insulating layer, the clue being that these insects are essentially desert and semi-desert dwellers. The camel's coat keeps in the heat during the cold nights in the desert and it also keeps out the heat of the sun by day. The female velvet ant, being wingless and forced to run over the hot sand by day, probably needs the insulating layer against the heat from the ground as well as from the sun. Her mate, in the case of most species of velvet ants, can keep cool by flying or perching in cooler air, but there are some species in which even the males have only degenerate knob-like wings, or are completely wingless.

AB Klots

Richard Cassell

phylum	**Arthropoda**
class	**Insecta**
order	**Hymenoptera**
family	**Mutillidae**

◁△ *Fur-coated in the desert: the hairs on the white desert velvet ant* **Dasymutilla gloriosa** *probably act as an insulating layer against the intense heat in the Arizona desert.*
◁ *A closer look shows that despite its ant-like attitude, its mouthparts are more typical of wasps.*

Venus' flower basket

The Venus' flower basket is the only deep-sea sponge at all well known outside scientific circles. In the second half of the 19th century its white, lacelike skeleton was treasured and given the place of honour in the best room in the house. It was also known as **regadéra,** the Spanish watering pot.

The 2 000 or more species of sponges live in marine and fresh waters, from between tidemarks to the depths of the oceans. The class to which the Venus' flower basket belongs is known as the Hexactinellida because they have a skeleton of six-rayed, or hexactin, spicules of silica. The Hexactinellida include most of the showy and beautifully delicate sponges as well as some of the largest and toughest. The Venus' flower basket skeleton is a 10in. curved tube, narrower at the base, where there is a tuft of hairlike spicules, and wider at the other end, which is closed by a perforated plate. This skeleton is covered by a thin layer of delicate flesh.

The Venus' flower basket lives in a relatively small area off the Philippines at depths of 600 ft. There are, however, related species in deep waters off Japan and in other parts of the western Pacific and the Indian Oceans.

▷ Like fine white porcelain — the beautiful lattice-like skeleton of a Venus's flower basket. The skeleton of this six-rayed sponge retains the general body structure and symmetry of the living animal. A convex perforated sieve-plate strengthens the upper end.

P Morris

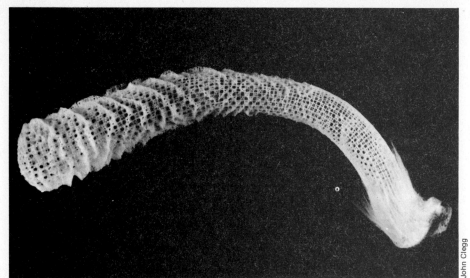

△ *A 10in. Venus' flower basket—the tuft of fibres at the lower end roots the living sponge.*

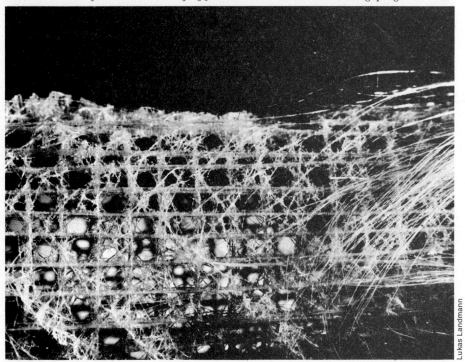

△ *Magnified: four of the six rays per spicule form this meshwork; the other two are tiny.*

How does it live?

The largest of the six-rayed spicules have four very long rays and two very short, the longs rays being interwoven to form a remarkable strut and girder work, revealed when the sponge is cleaned of its flimsy flesh. This was once described by a professor of engineering as 'the finest example of civil engineering ever seen, combining maximum strength with minimum material'. The tuft of long slender spicules at the base of a Venus' flower basket is like glass wool, but each strand ends in a minute anchorhead, visible only under a microscope. The whole tuft is probably embedded in soft mud. Water flows through holes in the wall of the tube into a central cavity and then out through the perforated plate. In other kinds of sponges (p 168) their flagellated chambers create a current which draws water into the body through one set of holes and drives it out again through another set. The flagellated chambers of hexactinellids are relatively large and thimble-shaped. Water flows passively through them. This led Dr George Bidder to suggest that the Venus' flower basket was not vertical to the seabed but that the curvature near its base meant it lay parallel to the sea floor.

Commonplace breeding

We can only presume that deep-sea sponges feed like sponges in shallower waters are believed to do, on minute particles of dead animal flesh or on bacteria, perhaps on both. Until 50 years ago even less was known about the breeding of Venus' flower basket. Then T Okada made a study of the whole life history of a related species. As in other sponges there are no special reproductive organs but sperms and ova are produced, in the breeding season, from body cells which grow much larger than usual. Presumably the sperms are released into the outgoing current, find their way to another sponge, enter it and fertilise the ova. These then divide repeatedly to form embryos which are released later as oval larvae that swim around for a while before settling on the bottom to grow into new sponges.

Enforced fidelity

The Japanese species studied by Okada has been linked with the species originally called the Venus' flower basket because the two are very alike. Both also have a pair of inch-long prawns inside them. These enter as larvae on the incoming water current, change into prawns, grow and then cannot get out. There may be up to three of these prawns inside a sponge but sometimes there is none. Most commonly there is a pair which, imprisoned for life, must remain together. So the sponge containing them has been accepted as a symbol of conjugal fidelity. In 1901, Professor Isao Ijima wrote that the sponges are in demand 'on account of an old custom connected with the marriage ceremony'. This was to include one of them in the decorations in the room where the marriage ceremony took place. 'It is held to be a felicitous object betokening eternal connubial love on account of the presence of the inmates in an inseparable pair. In the long list of gifts which the present Emperor and the Empress of Japan received from their subjects on the occasion of their twenty-fifth wedding anniversary are mentioned several *Euplectella*, gifts humble in themselves but full of well-wishing sentiments.'

Wiped out for money

The sponge first called the Venus' flower basket, and the one brought in numbers to Europe, came from a small area 'about a quarter of a mile' off Zebu, Philippines. Captain William Chimmo RN, writing in 1878, suggested it had been fished out of existence. If this were true only avarice could be blamed. The first specimens sold to Europeans fetched £10 a pair. This led to a minor 'gold rush'; the market was glutted and the sponge lost its high value.

A fabulous sponge

Another related deep-sea sponge, from the Indian Ocean, has an equally romantic name. It is called *Regadrella phoenix*, the first part of the name meaning a small Spanish watering pot, the second part alluding to the legend of the phoenix. This was a mythical bird said to appear every 500 years to build a nest and then set fire to it. The phoenix was consumed in the flames but from its ashes arose a new phoenix. When the sponge *Regadrella phoenix* dies several buds are formed at its base and each may grow into a new sponge. This species must also have a limited distribution because very few specimens have been dredged up.

phylum	**Parazoa**
class	**Nuda**
order	**Hexactinellida**
family	**Euplectellidae**
genus & species	***Euplectella aspergillum*** *Venus' flower basket* ***E. oweni**, others*

Vesper bat

There are 980 species of bats in 17
families. Nearly one-third of the species
are in one family, the Vespertilionidae.
They are usually referred to by those
studying bats as the vespertilionids but it
is not surprising that people with no
special knowledge of them have simplified
this to vesper bats. Since most of the 980
species of bats are seen in the evening,
this simplified name is hardly specific;
yet it is a convenient name for the small,
commonplace, insectivorous bats seen
especially in temperate latitudes, but found
all over the world except at the poles.

Vesper bats are mainly small. They
range from $1\frac{1}{4} - 4$ in. head and body
length, with wingspans of about $5 - 15$ in.
Most of them are various shades of brown,
sometimes grey or black, and a few are
yellow, orange or red. Some, like the
spotted or pinto bat of the United States
and Mexico, have white patches. Vesper
bats typically lack nose leaves but have
an earlet. The ears, as in the barbastelle
and the long-eared bat, may be up to
$1\frac{1}{2}$ in., half the length of head and body.

Leisler's bat **Nyctalus leisleri** hunting.

Photos by SC Bisserot

Sleeping quarters

Most vesper bats spend the daylight hours in caves or cavities in hollow trees, under loose bark, among foliage, or, more especially, in rock crevices, buildings, tunnels, mine shafts and natural caves. They usually hang by their hindfeet and prefer to sleep on a vertical face rather than hanging free by the toes. Some are solitary but most roost in small groups or in colonies. The sexes often roost separately, especially when the females are giving birth or have young. Roosting places are often traditional, with the same colony using a particular place year after year. Some species move from a summer feeding ground to winter quarters, which may be several miles away. The red and hoary bats make long migrations southwards at the end of summer, returning the following spring.

Highly manoeuvrable wings

A bat's skeleton is light. The arm, which carries the wing membrane, consists of a short upper arm and a long forearm with a single bone, the radius, and a compact wrist with several of the bones fused together. The finger bones are greatly elongated, especially the third and fourth, which support most of the wing membrane. The thumb is short and bears a claw, used in climbing or walking. The wing membrane runs from shoulder to wrist, over the fingers and backwards along the side of the body to the ankle. It is made up of a double layer of skin between which are such slender elastic strands and fine muscle fibres that the wing collapses and folds up easily when not in use. While on the wing, however, a bat has full control through the tendons, which are worked by the arm muscles, controlling all the joints; it is, in fact, the most manoeuvrable of all flying animals. Among vesper bats there are the long-eared bats that fly through foliage and hover to pick insects off leaves and, at the other extreme, the slender winged noctule that often hawks high-flying insects.

While the bat is flying its wing acts as a ventilator; the network of fine blood vessels allows the blood to be cooled so the bat does not become overheated from the exertion of flying. When the bat lands and folds its wings the flow of blood to the wings is cut down, so the heat is retained in the bat's body as the surface area is reduced.

Feeding on the wing

Nearly all vesper bats are insect-eaters. They have sharp teeth, the molars having a W-shaped pattern of cusps for chewing. One species, the fishing bat of California, eats fish and small crustaceans, and a few other species are suspected of catching fish. The desert bats of North America catch insects near the ground and also capture scorpions and lizards. Most vesper bats eat only insects, which they catch in flight. Small insects are chewed and swallowed straight away. Larger prey such as moths and beetles is usually pouched in the interfemoral membrane, between the tail and the hindlegs, where the bat, being able to bend its head back under its body, can chew it while in flight.

Members of the Vespertilionidae come out at varying times in the evening, from just before sundown to almost dark. Some are still seen on the wing just before dawn, but

the night is divided into alternating spells of hunting and resting to digest their food. Some species, like the noctule, have only two periods of hunting, of an hour each.

Delayed fertilisation

Most of our information about the breeding of vesper bats is from species in temperate regions, where the bats hibernate. There, mating usually takes place between August and October, the sperms being stored in the female, and it may also occur again in spring. All fertilisation is in spring and after a gestation of 40–70 days, or even 100, according to the species, the babies are born from late May to July. In the tropics fertilisation follows immediately after mating. The number of babies at a birth is usually one or two, but there may be four.

Accidents in the dark

Because they fly by night bats probably have few enemies. Hawks have occasionally been seen to take them, well before nightfall. Owls have taken others, after dark. Domestic cats have on occasion been seen leaping

up to capture a bat venturing too near the ground, so presumably wildcats sometimes take them. Despite the efficient echo-location system by which they find their prey and locate obstacles in pitch dark, there are records of bats seen flying into walls breaking their necks. Such accidents may be more frequent than we suspect.

Rip van Winkle bats

As a result of banding hibernating whiskered bats in the caves in Holland we know that 40% die in the first six months of life and beyond this the average expectation of life is about $4\frac{1}{2}$ years, but some of the bats have lived to 20 years or more. This is a remarkably long time compared with other small mammals of similar size, such as shrews and mice, which live only a few years, about five years in the longest-lived. The bat's effective life is, however, very brief. A noctule, for example, spends about six months of the year hibernating. In the remaining six months it is on the wing for about two hours in every 24.

◁△ *Reconnaissance: a noctule bat* **Nyctalus noctula** *looks, listens and sniffs before takeoff. The sharp teeth crush beetles, a favourite item in the noctule's diet.*
△ *European longeared bat, showing the skin 'bag' between the legs, which acts as both net and aerial larder in which to pouch large or hard insects on the wing.*

class	**Mammalia**
order	**Chiroptera**
family	**Vespertilionidae**
genera & species	***Antrozous pallidus*** *desert bat* ***Barbastella barbastellus*** *barbastelle* ***Lasiurus borealis*** *red bat* ***L. cinereus*** *hoary bat* ***Myotis mystacinus*** *whiskered bat* ***Nyctalus noctula*** *noctule* ***Pizonyx vivesi*** *fishing bat* ***Plecotus auritus*** *longeared (European)* ***P. macrotis*** *longeared (American), others*

Vine pest

When Columbus discovered America he started a chain of events that nearly ruined the vineyards of France. Native to North America, the vine pest is a tiny insect related to the well-known aphides, also known as plant lice, greenfly and blackfly. The vine pest is called the vine phylloxera, sometimes referred to as the graperoot louse, although it also feeds on a wide range of other plants.

Except that the vine pest threatened to wipe out the vine-growing industry in France and elsewhere towards the end of the last century, there is little that is remarkable about it, other than its complicated life history. The vine pest was introduced into Europe between 1858 and 1863, when vine growers were experimenting with species of vines imported from America. By 1885 it had reached Algeria, Australia and South Africa. It also reached California about the same time, probably taken there on vines from other parts of the United States east of the Rocky Mountains that had been imported from Europe.

▽ Ugly galls on the lower surface of a dried vine leaf, destructive work of the vine pest.
▽▷ The culprits, wingless and winged females.
▽▽ Healthy looking grape vines in Yugoslavia

Crown Copyright

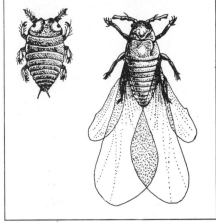

Chris Howell-Jones

Picturepoint

Nearly vineyards' doomsday

From time immemorial only one species of vine has ever been used for wine-making in Europe. This is *Vitis vinifera*, a native of the region bordering the Caspian Sea, and it has proved extremely susceptible to attacks of the introduced vine pest. The presence of the aphid on a vine is shown first by the stunting of the plant itself and then in the reduction in the size and number of the leaves. In some cases the leaves become discoloured and galls form on their lower surfaces. At the same time knot-like swellings are found on the smaller roots. These turn from yellow to black and cause the roots to die and decay. The growth of the grapes is arrested and the fruits become wrinkled. When at its worst this pest ruined 2½ million acres of vineyards in France.

A complicated life history

After mating the female vine pest aphid lays her egg on the bark of the vine. Each egg passes the winter on the bark and in spring hatches, producing a wingless female called a fundatrix, or foundress. This female crawls into a leaf bud where she causes a gall to develop on the young leaf. Inside the gall she lays a number of eggs which develop into further wingless females called gallicolae, or gall-dwellers. These multiply during the summer, giving further gall-forming generations that in turn infest other leaves. Later in the season they produce another kind of wingless female, the radicicolae, or root-dwellers, which go down to the roots. After producing several generations of their own kind these radicicolae give rise to winged females which, in late summer, fly to other vines where they lay two kinds of eggs: small ones which produce males and large ones which produce females, both sexes being again wingless. The mouth-parts and digestive systems of this latest batch are not developed so they do not feed, but they mate and each female lays a single egg. These are the eggs which overwinter and which form the start of a new generation of fundatrix females which start the whole complex series again.

This is the typical, complete life history of a vine pest on its natural and native American host plants. When transferred to European vines the radicicolae are the principal form and they seem to be able to hibernate through the winter and reproduce their own kind indefinitely.

How it is controlled

The French vineyards are, happily, still productive. They were saved by intensive entomological research. There are many species of vine native to North America and these have varying degrees of resistance to the vine phylloxera. If European vines are grafted onto stocks of these resistant American plants the radicicolae are unable to thrive on their roots and the *Vitis vinifera* scions escape the effects of the pest. *V. riparia*, *V. rupestris* and *V. berlandieri* are American species of vine that are suitable for grafting, and hybrids between them and *V. vinifera* are also extensively used.

In the American grape-growing industry *V. vinifera* is cultivated on resistant stocks, as in Europe, and some resistant species of vines, producing fruit of different kinds and flavours, are also grown, including *V. labrusca* and *V. rotundifolia*.

Dangers of easy living

Aphides in general, and the vine pest in particular, have specialized mainly in the simple life. As insects go they are simple in structure, having few specializations other than the general features of the Hemiptera, the order to which they belong. Their food is simple and so is their method of feeding: they simply push their proboscis into the skin of a plant and suck. So, apart from enemies, life would be idyllic. By contrast, their methods of reproduction are highly complicated. Some pests have even more complicated life histories. The oak phylloxera, *Phylloxera quercus,* has no fewer than 21 different forms in its life history.

Complicated life histories, coupled with a high rate of multiplication, tend to be the rule for parasites. This can mean only one thing: that a complex reproductive cycle is needed for the species to survive. It is an indication that parasitism may bring an easy living but it is a precarious way of life.

phylum	**Arthropoda**
class	**Insecta**
order	**Hemiptera**
family	**Phylloxeridae**
genus & species	***Phylloxera vitifoliae*** *vine pest*

Viperfish

The deepsea viperfishes are a fearsome sight because of their long fanglike teeth, which are slightly barbed at their tips. The teeth project on either side of the jaws.

The body of a viperfish ranges from 6—10 in. long, but its slender build makes it appear longer and it is only slightly thicker behind the head than in the tail. The head is small but has a strong lower jaw. The fins, including the tailfin, are also small, the pectorals being smaller than the pelvics. There is a small adipose fin, just in front of the tailfin, and opposite this on the underside are two small anal fins set close together. The most prominent fin is the first dorsal, set just behind the level of the rear end of the pectoral fins and it has a long whiplike spine formed from the first ray of the fin. The spine is about half the length of the fish and carries a small light organ at its tip. A double row of light organs runs all along either side of the lower body edge.

They live from 1 500—9 000 ft in oceans between latitudes 60° N and 40° S.

Popperfoto

Viper or pike of the deep seas?

Usually, deepsea animals can be studied only from their dead bodies brought to the surface in nets. We are a little better off with viperfishes because we have the brief sightings by William Beebe who made the first descent into the ocean and saw one through the window of his bathysphere in 1934. In his book *Half Mile Down* he spoke of seeing a fine red prawn that was pounced upon by a 'really fearsome' viperfish which shook it for a moment then swallowed it. He also spoke of the viperfish's stomach that can stretch enormously as if it were made of rubber. The long body of a viperfish, with the second dorsal and the anal fins set far back, recalls the pike in fresh waters, which lunges swiftly at its prey, seizing it in a wide mouth armed with fearsome teeth. On the other hand a viperfish also has a lure—the light organ at the end of its whiplike dorsal spine—presumably used for tempting prey within reach. It also has 350 tiny light organs in the roof of its mouth and on the lower surface of the eyeball. Presumably these attract crustaceans and small fish near enough so when it opens its mouth to take in water for breathing they are drawn in. Thus a viperfish feeds as it breathes—at least so far as small prey is concerned.

Opening its throat

In the early 1950's Dr VV Tchernavin completed his brilliant anatomical studies of the viperfishes. He showed that the first vertebra behind the head is large and has broad surfaces for the attachment of strong muscles. The backbone, immediately behind this, is supple. The heart is well forward and lies between the bones of the lower jaw, as do the gills. In swallowing prey the muscles attached to the first vertebra pull the head up and, with the mouth opening at the same time, the lower jaw is shot forward, so the head seems almost to part company with the body as the throat opens at the sides. The effect is to give a wide and clear passage into the gullet. At the same time the heart is carried forward and the delicate gills outward, so they are not damaged by prey, even large prey, entering the throat. When the prey has been swallowed the head, jaws, heart and gills all return to their normal position. It is reasonable to suppose that with so much derangement of the vital organs, the swallowing action must be rapid. Digestion also seems to be very quick since most of these fishes have empty stomachs when caught.

Competition in depth

There are 300 million cubic miles of water in the oceans, room enough for the deepsea animals to be well spaced out. The study of many viperfishes suggests that in spite of all this space the various species are in competition with each other. There are three species of viperfishes. They are *Chauliodus danae*, *C. barbatus* and *C. sloani*, and the last of these is divided into 5 subspecies, two of which are *C. sloani sloani* and *C. sloani schmidti*. These two and *C. danae* live in the Atlantic, but each has its definite range which can be marked out on a map. In places their ranges are contiguous or even overlapping and where this happens it affects their vertical distribution. For example, in areas where *C. sloani sloani* is on its own it lives between 1 500 and 9 000 ft during the day—all viperfishes migrate into the surface layers at night. Where this is in the same area as *C. danae* it occupies only the depth from 3 000 to 5 400 ft, and *C. danae* occupies the rest.

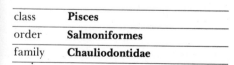

class	**Pisces**
order	**Salmoniformes**
family	**Chauliodontidae**

◁ *A weird appearance is given by viperfishes because of their long fanglike teeth. This appearance has often led to them being used as illustrations of deepsea fishes although there are only three species of viperfishes and they certainly do not represent all the varied and numerous deepsea animal forms. The photophores or light organs can be clearly seen running along the side of the body as a double row and nearly extend to the tail. The three species of viperfishes occur in all oceans between latitudes 60° N and 40° S from tropical to very cold water and between 1 500 and 9 000 ft. Species: Chauliodus sloani*

Vireo

Vireos are small, drably plumaged song-birds of the New World. The 42 species, together with the little-known shrike-vireos and peppershrikes, make up the family Vireonidae. In the 19th century they were known as greenlets but this name is now used for only tropical vireos of the genus **Hylophilus.** Vireos range from 4 to 7 in. long and are usually olive-green or grey above and whitish or yellowish underneath. The bill is slender and sometimes bears a hook.

The best known is the red-eyed vireo, 6 in. long, olive-green above and whitish underneath. The top of the head is slate-grey and there is a white line with a black border running over the red eye. It breeds from central Canada to the shores of the Gulf of Mexico but is missing from most of the western half of the United States. One of the brightest vireos is the yellow-throated vireo of the eastern United States. It is olive-green above with two white wing bars, a yellow eye-stripe and yellow on the chin, throat and breast. The greenlets are among the smallest vireos. The grey-headed greenlet is 4 in. long with a grey head and a white ring around the eye. The body is olive-green above and white and yellow underneath.

The vireos range from central Canada to northern Argentina, including the West Indies and the Bahamas and the slender-billed vireo is confined to the tiny island of Fernando de Noronha, 250 miles off the Brazilian coastline.

◁◁ *Devoted to incubation, this red-eyed vireo will not easily be persuaded to leave its nest — vireos have very strong parental urges. The nest is a deep cup of grass and strips of bark in which 3 or 4 spotted eggs are laid.*
◁ *The white-eyed vireo **Vireo griseus** has drab plumage typical of most of the family.*
◁▽ *An adult red-eyed vireo tries to satisfy the insatiable. The nestlings are fed mainly on insects and the parents share the task of food-collecting, although usually, as here, it is the female who works the harder.*

zontal fork by cobwebs. The female does most of the building and lays a clutch of 3 or 4 eggs in temperate regions or 2 or 3 eggs in the tropics. They are white or cream with brown or lilac spots. Incubation lasts 12 — 14 days and the male helps, although he sits for a shorter time than the female. The males are such dedicated singers that they even sing while sitting on the nest. Not all males incubate, however, and in those species in which males do not share incubation they do not brood the young either. Otherwise, the urge to incubate is very strong and vireos sometimes have to be lifted off the nest in order to count their eggs. They may even peck at the offending hand. The chicks are fed by both parents, the female bringing most of the food, and they start to fly when about 2 weeks old.

Trans-Atlantic immigrants

Although their distribution is American, red-eyed vireos occasionally turn up in the British Isles, especially on the western coast of Ireland and on the Scilly Isles, off the southwestern tip of England. The red-eyed vireo is one of a growing band of American birds that have been seen in the British Isles. These new migrants include the pectoral sandpiper *Erolia melanotos*, various ducks and cuckoos, the American robin, the bobolink *Dolichonyx oryzivorus* and the Baltimore oriole *Icterus galbula*. Shore birds and water birds might be expected to make the crossing but many trans-Atlantic migrants are small passerines. Some may have escaped from local aviaries but others definitely have not. It has been suggested that, having been blown out to sea, these small birds hitch lifts on ships for the rest of the way. However, they could not survive so long without food, many being insect-eaters, and if hitch-hiking were the answer, there should be as many records of European birds reaching North America. In fact, there seems to be a very good reason for thinking that the vireos and others are swept high across the Atlantic by the jet-streams in a few hours. Probably whole flocks are caught up but few birds make a landfall.

Monotonous songs
Except for some, like the red-eyed vireo, which lives in trees, most vireos live in undergrowth or thickets. They are not easy to see as they flit through the foliage, their drab colours making them 'just another small brown bird' to all but bird watchers, who often find it easier to identify them by their voice or habits.

A few vireos have pleasant songs, such as that of the warbling vireo of North America and the brown-capped vireo of tropical America. The songs of these two birds are continuous warblings. The other vireos are also persistent songsters but there is little that is musical about them. The red-eyed vireo was once known as 'the preacher' from its boring, rambling utterances. Each phrase consists of a variety of half a dozen notes, and one indefatigable ornithologist counted 22 917 phrases from one red-eyed vireo in one day. This was an average of over 1 000 an hour. The white-eyed vireo varies its collection of clicks and mews with mimicked notes of other birds.

Many of the North American vireos are migratory, spending the winter in Central America. The red-eyed vireo migrates across the Gulf of Mexico, down Central America and into South America as far as southern Brazil.

Foliage searchers
Vireos feed mainly on insects, their larvae, spiders and a few small fruits. The insects and spiders are sought among the foliage which the vireos move through with agility, sometimes hanging upside down to search the undersides of leaves. Large insects are held down with one foot and attacked by thrusting and tearing with the bill. Only rarely do vireos search for food on the ground. Red-eyed vireos sometimes descend to feed on small snails.

Singing on the nest
The nest is built in a tree or bush, sometimes near the ground but never on it. It is a deep cup of grass, leaves, strips of bark and other materials and is slung in a hori-

class	**Aves**
order	**Passeriformes**
family	**Vireonidae**
genera & species	*Hylophilus decurtatus* grey-headed greenlet *Vireo gilvus* warbling vireo *V. flavifrons* yellow-throated vireo *V. gracilirostris* slender-billed vireo *V. olivaceus* red-eyed vireo others

Viscacha

The plains viscacha and mountain viscacha are South American rodents closely related to the chinchilla (p 432). They are different in both form and habitat. The plains viscacha is heavily-built; an adult male may weigh as much as 15 lb. The body is up to 2 ft long with a short 6–8in. tail. The head is large and blunt with prominent black whiskers. The tail, which is fully furred, is short and stiff and helps the animal to sit upright. The four fingers on the forefeet are well-developed for burrowing and the three toes on the hindfeet have very sharp claws. The fur is coarse and fairly long, dark grey above with white underparts and black and white stripes on the face. The female is smaller with somewhat lighter fur.

The mountain viscacha, sometimes called the mountain chinchilla, looks more like a chinchilla or a long-tailed rabbit. It is smaller than its plains relative, 12½–15¾ in. long in head and body with a long tail, up to 12½ in. It is a much slighter animal, weighing up to only 3½ lb. It has large, erect ears and unlike the plains viscacha the claws on the fore- and hindfeet are blunt and weak. The fur is short, thick and soft. The upper parts vary from fawn to dark grey and the underparts are whitish, yellow or light grey. There is a crest of stiff hairs on the tail, which is black to reddish brown, and it often has a black stripe down the back.

*Today there is only one species of plains viscacha, found over most of Argentina, and spreading into southern Brazil. Another species **Lagostomus crassus** is now almost certainly extinct. The four species of mountain viscacha are found in the Andes and its foothills, up to a height of 17 000 ft, from Peru and Bolivia southward to the Argentine.*

Social animals

Both the plains and mountain viscacha live in colonies, the former on the pampas and scrubland and the latter in rugged, mountainous country wherever water and food are available. The plains viscacha digs extensive burrows, with long tunnels and numerous entrances, known as viscacheras. Some have been in continual use for centuries and sometimes cover as much as 200 sq ft. Colonies of 15–30 individuals are usually formed, ruled over by a single adult male. They are very clean rodents, carrying all their refuse up to pile on the excavated earth at the entrance to the burrow. The entire surrounding area is cleared and they seem to have a passion for collecting objects and adorning the earth mounds with them. Stones, bones, cow-dung, branches and even objects accidentally dropped by man are dragged to the burrows and placed on top of the mounds.

The plains viscacha is nocturnal, coming out to feed in the evening. It shares its

▷ *The range of the mountain viscacha extends over mountainous country high in the Andes, and is quite separate from that of the pampas-dwelling plains viscacha.*

△ △ *The two kinds of viscacha differ in appearance as well as in habitat. A big head with short ears and a distinctive facial stripe are the most noticeable features of the portly plains viscacha, in contrast with its smaller mountain cousin (overleaf). Plains viscachas construct large mounds over their warrens, which were once scattered over the pampas in such numbers as to create a serious hazard to horsemen. Objects of all kinds are collected by the viscachas and displayed on the mounds.*

△ *Unlike the mountain viscacha, the plains viscacha produces only one litter a year, and the two offspring are slower to mature.*

◁ *Portrait of an inveterate collector.*

Viscacha

■ Mountain
(Lagidium peruanum)

▨ Plains
(Lagostomus maximus)

△ *The chinchilla-like mountain viscacha is less houseproud than the plains viscacha. It does not excavate warrens, but lives in rock crevices high in the mountains.*

burrows with many other creatures; owls, snakes, lizards and even skunks. It is also friendly with its own kind and occupants of neighbouring colonies visit each other during the night. It has a variety of calls from grunts and squeals to a wire-twanging sound. The warning note is a peculiar swishing noise followed by a liquid note which sounds like a drop of water falling into a pool.

The mountain viscachas have a very different way of life. Although living in colonies of up to 80 individuals they do not burrow but shelter in rock crevices or among piles of boulders. Unlike their relatives on the plains they are diurnal and spend most of the day basking in the sun. They feed in the evenings but always return to shelter before dark. They are very agile, running among the rocks and leaping up the mountainside with their long hindlegs.

Devastation of grassland
The plains viscachas feed on a wide variety of grasses, roots, stems and seeds. They are voracious feeders, often laying bare large areas of grassland. In captivity they will also take carrot and potato. The mountain viscachas feed on plants—grasses, moss and lichens found near their colonies.

Slow breeding
The plains viscacha is a slow breeder. After a gestation of slightly less than 5 months, two young are born in September. There is only one litter a year and the young do not reach maturity for 2 years. The mountain viscacha mates in October and November and usually only a single young is born after a gestation of about 3 months, but there may be 2 or 3 litters a year. The young are able to nibble plants an hour after birth and males become sexually mature in 7 months.

Plains viscacha on the blacklist
Now that the puma has disappeared from its range the plains viscacha has virtually no enemy except man. Owing to the wide devastation of areas by the rodent's burrowing and its voracious appetite for grass it is now regarded as a serious pest and in the past few years it has been cleared from many areas of Argentina, especially where grazing animals are kept. It is not eaten by the local people nor is its fur valuable but a few years ago canned viscacha began to be exported to Italy where it proved to be very popular.

The mountain viscacha on the other hand is hunted by the local people for food and for its hair which is mixed with wool and made into a yarn. It also has a natural enemy in the Andean fox. All species are now sparsely distributed throughout their range and the mountain viscacha, in particular, seems in some danger of extinction.

Live trapping
Various methods of exterminating the plains viscacha have been tried out, including stopping up the entrances to starve the animals out and flooding. In a fairly recent expedition to obtain live animals for study, because so little is known about them, several methods of catching live viscachas were tried out, including digging out and vibration. The only methods that met with any success were flooding and trapping. Some were caught as they fled from their viscachera after it had been flooded but the majority were caught by trapping. All the holes to the viscachera were stopped up and wire-mesh treadle traps set at the most-frequented holes. The traps were examined at dawn and dusk and re-set in fresh holes if no animals had been caught after two visits. This method caught two or three viscachas every day until a total of 151 animals had been captured.

class	**Mammalia**
order	**Rodentia**
family	**Chinchillidae**
genera & species	***Lagidium peruanum*** *mountain viscacha* ***Lagostomus maximus*** *plains viscacha, others*